D0734340
TWENTIETH CENTURY LIBRARY
WITHDRAWN

Twentieth Century Library

Charles Darwin

PAUL B. SEARS

Charles Darwin

THE NATURALIST AS A CULTURAL FORCE

CHARLES SCRIBNER'S SONS, NEW YORK

CHARLES SCRIBNER'S SONS, LTD., LONDON

1950

Printed in the United States of America

Quotation on page 19, reprinted from LUCRETIUS: On the Nature of Things, translated by W. E. Leonard, No. 750 in Everyman's Library; used by permission of E. P. Dutton & Co., Inc., New York and J. M. Dent & Sons, Ltd., London, publishers.

To Frederick Orville Grover, Botanist

and

Edward Loranus Rice, Zoologist

Students and Interpreters of Charles Darwin

ACKNOWLEDGMENTS

I am indebted to many friends for substantial assistance. But particular thanks are due to Mr. Thomas LeDuc for information regarding Winchell, Woodrow, and Peirce; to Miss Zita Mueller for checking of source material; to Messrs. Harry J. Fuller and J. A. Detlefson for technical information; to Mrs. Elizabeth Fuller for her skillful and intelligent help in preparing copy; and to Mr. Charles Scribner, Jr. for his ready editorial cooperation. Thanks are also due to E. P. Dutton & Co., Inc., New York, for permission to quote from William Ellery Leonard's translation of Lucretius *On the Nature of Things.*

Whether there is justification for the considerable effort of Mr. Hiram Haydn, Editor of this series, without whose persuasion the book would not have been attempted, time will tell.

CONTENTS

Charles Darwin

FOREWORD

THE RIGHT TO SEE

"IN conclusion," said Bishop Wilberforce, "I should like to ask my honorable opponent whether he considers himself descended from a monkey on his grandmother's side or his grandfather's." Whereupon Thomas Huxley, who called himself Darwin's Bulldog, arose to his feet. ". . . . a man," said he, "has no reason to be ashamed of having an ape for his grandfather. If there were an ancestor whom I should feel shame in recalling, it would be a *man,* a man of restless and versatile intellect, who, not content with an equivocal success in his own sphere of activity, plunges into scientific questions with which he has no real acquaintance, only to obscure them by an aimless rhetoric, and distract the attention of his hearers from the real point at issue by eloquent digressions, and skilled appeals to religious prejudice."

It would be impossible to state the issue more clearly. Huxley's genius had compressed the real meaning of Darwin's life and work into one devastating sentence. He had carried matters back to first principles—back of any mass of scientific evidence, back of any doctrine which might be drawn from that evidence—to the question of ultimate human dignity.

So long as scientists had confined their attention to the physical world, or even to a description of living things without getting too inquisitive as to the meaning of life, the leaders of Victorian England had been content to leave them unmolested, and more than content to enjoy the practical fruits of their labors. But when scientific curiosity turned towards deeper questions, and began to pry apart the assumptions on which the dominant part of Victorian society rested so comfortably, the vials of wrath were unstopped.

The zealous guardians of official faith bestirred themselves and though that faith was Christian, built square upon the dignity and responsibility of the individual, its spokesmen aligned themselves against the full expression of this principle. They were unwilling to trust the worth and integrity of the individual human mind.

The question of spiritual worth—the right to a place in Heaven (on terms, to be sure) had been settled. So, in growing measure, had the question of political worth. The problems of social and economic dignity were assuredly coming up. But Darwin had really hit the center of the whole business—the right of the individual to trust his own eyes, and form his own judgments, tell the world his belief, and have the matter cleared by open trial and honest evidence. This was the essence of the Darwinian revolution. The other issues it raised were really incidental. Yet they, too, were vastly important.

Before Darwin could attempt to free the minds of others, he had to free his own. He was a product of his own time, a part of his own culture. There is mischief in the idea of solitary, insulated genius. To know how Darwin has helped to change our world of today, we must have a glimpse of the world of thought in which he grew up and we must trace, not only his experiences, but those threads of reflection and understanding which he picked up from others and wove into the fabric of his own mind.

We shall have to reckon, too, with the accelerating complexity of the modern world and the innumerable influences which are shaping it. To put the finger on specific effects as flowing from specific things that Darwin uttered would be casuistry, if not nonsense. It would certainly be a betrayal of Darwin's own meticulous ideals of inquiry.

The best we can hope to do is to examine ourselves, and try

to see wherein our behavior and our modes of thinking, our values, and our sanctions, reflect the point of view which Darwin represents. He would have been the last to claim this viewpoint as his exclusive property, but he most certainly brought it into focus, made it reasonable. In this sense he personifies a great cooperative social and intellectual movement. Life today is vastly changed by this movement, and some of the more obvious changes, at least, we may be able to identify.

A PUZZLED WORLD

CHARLES DARWIN and Abraham Lincoln were born on the same day of the year 1809. The Battle of Waterloo, still six years in the future, was to inaugurate a century of relative but by no means absolute peace. The 19th century was destined to be one of amazing technical progress, although the years 1809–1909 probably brought less fundamental change in everyday living than have the succeeding forty years, 1909–1949. It is during these past forty or fifty years that the impact of modern science has been really overwhelming.

The French Revolution had been neatly diverted into an imperial dictatorship which had Europe in turmoil. The American Revolution was *fait accompli*. The British Revolution begun by Cromwell had long since settled down to its phlegmatic, parliamentary course, while the Royal Navy was efficiently acquiring possessions and trade-territory, and policing the high seas. Germany and Russia were well-behaved partners in the struggle against Napoleon; Italy and Spain passive battlegrounds. Japan and the rest of the Orient slept calmly. The Roman Church had reached one of the lowest levels of influence in its long history.

Western Europe was shifting from rural to urban economy. Coal, steam, and steel were taking over, factories replacing the craftsman's shop. The rest of the world was glad to exchange food and raw materials for the products of the new industrialism. Yet the motive power for transport and travel was still wind by sea, and muscle by land. The great era of railroad building had not begun.

The physical comforts and safeguards of the rich, in spite

of an abundance of well-trained servants, were scarcely equal to those in a modest farm-house or factory-worker's dwelling today. Life expectancy was half what it is now, with the causes of infectious diseases such as typhoid and malaria unknown, and the importance of pure water and balanced diet but dimly guessed. Surgery, even the best, was a nightmare, without anaesthetics or X-rays. High rates of infant mortality and frequent death in childbirth were accepted with resignation as the Will of God.

Although printing had been known for four hundred years, education was still a privilege, like good food, clothing and travel, to be reserved for those who could afford it. A few charitable foundations might provide, or exceptional determination secure, its benefits to children of the poor. Even the best education then available was curiously rigid and limited. It had merit, emphasizing as it did the importance of the past, and it made one concession to science—mathematics. Latin, Greek, History, Logic, Rhetoric and various aspects of Moral Philosophy (see p. 6) were heavily emphasized. Experimental science (Natural Philosophy) and Natural History lagged behind. There was a good deal of impressive, at times, luminous, scholarship. But with such obvious worship of the past, a great deal of untested, *a priori*, material was taught, even in the sciences. There was little in the undergraduate curriculum to encourage free inquiry, as a rule.

The learned professions, open to gentlemen in England, were law, medicine, and the ministry, with teaching as a possible fourth. All other occupations, and in a measure even law and medicine, were to be learned by apprenticeship. Thus formal scientific training had the status of a necessary evil, ancillary to medicine. Many of the contemporary scientists were physicians. Most of the remainder were amateurs, trained by their own reading and experiments, and by exchange of ideas with friends of like tastes. While the system doubtless had its advantages, it offered no check on dilettantes of wealth and position. The Royal Society, which had been sponsored in 1660 by Charles II—possibly in the sly hope that it might conjure up wealth for that impecunious monarch—had included from the first a group of reputable working scientists. But social prestige plus a very superficial interest in science often entitled gentlemen to election, thus diluting the quality of membership to a considerable degree.

An even greater difficulty lay in the fact that few, even of the professional scientists, could escape the limitations of their classical training. At its best, such training gives a sense of historical continuity and of human values, along with a respect for language. Even in its least inspired form it is likely to make some contribution to clear and accurate reading and utterance. But the definitions of words and the relations between words, important as they are, are only a part of understanding. Words refer to things and relationships in the world around us, and without convincing, first-hand, experience of the phenomena of that world, understanding is not reasonably complete. Thus, quite apart from the training of professional scientists, the education of 1809 was inadequate for the needs of the intelligent layman, as much so-called higher education still is.

The prevailing division of knowledge and therefore the basis of the faculties was four-fold. All recorded fact was history. All search for meaning was philosophy. All knowledge about man was moral, and all other knowledge was natural. Thus we have the possible combinations:

Moral history—the record of man
Moral philosophy—the significance of human life and experience
Natural history—the record of nature
Natural philosophy—the interpretation of nature.

Admirable in its emphasis on human values as moral, this system did not allow for the possibility of viewing man as a part of nature. Man was not to be studied by the impersonal methods of science even for his own good. Not until the sixteenth century, and then only through the daring enterprise of Vesalius, had there been much systematic knowledge of human anatomy. And during Darwin's active life, the very group that objected most strenuously to any suggestion of man's kinship with other animals greatly impeded the course of physiology by their prejudice against animal experimentation. Yet their formula allowed an ill-trained doctor to do his ignorant and bloody best on human patients! The soul, which could not be seen, weighed, nor measured, was the thing. The body was left to take its chances.

Thus the sentry-boxes of society were manned by the guardians of the soul. Uniforms, drill regulations, and regimental allegiance might vary with time and place. An accommodation with earthly reality was generally worked out, provided always that spiritual authority was not damaged. The divinity of kings had gone, but the duty of humbly accepting one's lot in life was still sternly imposed. When matters became too intolerable, there were reforms and adjustments, to be sure. The then moribund Church of England had neglected the orphaned masses of the poor, so Wesley and Whitefield nobly took over that responsibility. (Only heroes risked the taint of "vulgarity" in 18th-century England.)

All praise to men who sincerely devote themselves to what they construe as the highest good of their fellow-men. But the difficulty—with the possible exception of the Quakers—was that in every case the welfare of the human soul was held to depend upon the acceptance of certain ideas about the nature of the universe, whether those ideas were compatible with physical experience or not. There had been, in the course of history, much adjustment to experience, but any compromise always faced powerful taboos. Clerical abuses and crude bigotry could be dealt with, but this gentle, affectionate, and all-pervasive insistence on higher truth was another matter. To question it was like trying to brush aside the roseate clouds which envelop mother-love.

There is a certain danger of injustice in wholly condemning the prolonged and powerful effort to guide human thought into *a priori* channels. Students of society and of psychology both agree on the necessity of a consistent, orderly system of certainties. It is at first startling to hear an anthropologist defend the superstitions of a primitive people on the grounds that, right or wrong, they afford a provisional framework of explanations. One must remember that no group can get along without its own inner consistencies, however crude such systems may seem to members of more enlightened groups. And the individual no less than the group must have certainty and consistency in his world. The sound of a bell has nothing to do with the biochemistry of nutrition. But if that sound has been associated with feeding habits and the pattern is disturbed, violent physiological results may ensue. Order is Heaven's first law.

Without belief in order there can be no science. Even science, which attempts to scrutinize the universe without prejudice, is to that extent itself an act of faith. Ironically, the viewpoint which Darwin was to champion was a product of the same forces which fought it so desperately. How did this come about?

The eastern Mediterranean is the cradle of European thought. Its ancient civilizations personified and worshipped (largely by placation) the seemingly inconsistent and conflicting forces of nature, whose chief was Baal. The operation of those forces, particularly under population pressure and recurrent food shortage, cost human lives. The sacrifice of infants to Baal was the ritualistic response to this cruel fact. (One can somehow guess at its inner logic after seeing the measure of comfort and acceptance at Mexican folk-funerals. In that country, with an exceedingly high infant mortality, it seems impossible to stay the hand of death. But it is possible to escort the tiny body with flowers and music and friends, and so the blow is cushioned.)

Eventually the Jews revolted against an acceptance of blind and ruthless conflict among the powers of the universe, with man as their hapless victim. They proclaimed a doctrine of unity, with a single God who embodied the highest ethical conceptions of which they themselves were capable. Their God was a God of law, respecting and personifying his own laws. The sacred writings of the Jews show how this idea grew in stature and moral significance, until it culminated in the Christian ideal of love.

Because the new faith of Judaism was a desperate revolt

against the worship of blind nature, the Jews in large measure set themselves apart from the rest of the natural world—indeed apart from the rest of mankind. Thus the significant thing was to learn the will of God directly rather than through a study of its manifestations in nature. The poet—called prophet—and not the scientist, became the medium through whom this will was to be learned. The opening chapters of Genesis are a magnificent poetic account of Earth's beginnings, but by no construction a scientific record.

This neglect of a study of nature, combined with reliance upon the poet, might have had disastrous consequences but for one thing. The Jews were intensely practical, and they developed their practical knowledge into a rigidly binding code of dietary and sanitary regulations. This, too, became a part of the will of God. It was empirical, but such good empiricism that scientific hindsight shows it to have been an important factor in the vitality and survival of this remarkable people. Without an interest in natural science, the Jews paved the way for future science by proclaiming the unity and universality of law.

The Greeks likewise began with nature worship, but carried on in a different mood. Their many Gods were retained, to form a rowdy pantheon, whose doings were not untinged with humor. But there was nothing humorous about the idea of the Fates who controlled both Gods and men. And the moral idea of Destiny grew in stature, as had the Hebrew conception of Jehovah, with the passing of time. In the end Greek civilization marched to its death, as much a victim of its moral obligation to defend the state as it was victim to its follies.

The Greek system, however, permitted a compromise which that of the Jews did not. How much this was due to physical conditions on the sunny islands of Greece, as compared with a narrow home on the somber margin of the desert, we can only guess. But in a sense, for the Greek, Gods and men were in the same boat, along with the rest of nature. Divinities were in the woods and waters, even susceptible to the charms of handsome men and beautiful women. There was nothing either impious or futile about human curiosity in such a game of hide-and-seek. So with the growth of leisure and intellectual discipline, the Greeks became an inquiring people, learning much of Nature and its laws. Except as individuals, however, they never broke through the barrier which Darwin was to crumble nearly two millennia later.

With them the barrier was not religious, but intellectual. Their greatest philosopher, Plato, held that ideas are the ultimate realities, and the physical world merely a clumsy expression of those ideas. As a working program for pedestrian science, this is pretty bad. It gives the abstract thinker the same priority over experience that the prophet enjoyed among the Jews, and has the same lofty appeal. Why should the troublesome, humdrum, petty evidence of the senses be allowed to modify the results of pure logic, or the exalted conceptions of the inspired poet?

True, the ideas of Plato were considerably modified by his pupil Aristotle, a keen, skillful biologist, and logician. But it is clear from reading the surviving works of this remarkable man that he was often uncritical in accepting evidence on scientific matters and much given to inference from preconceived ideas. Thus the conflicts of Victorian England had their roots deep in an ancient past.

When Greece collapsed, Rome took over, inheriting the premises but remodelling to suit her own genius. That genius was practical, concerned with political housekeeping. Housekeeping is properly a means to an end, but can become an end in itself. To a degree, this was true of the Romans. All values, even virtue itself, were subordinated to the concept of order in the realm. In the end Roman civilization developed many of the symptoms of a meticulous, rich, and frustrated widow. In her bleak spiritual emptiness she turned finally to a new faith, preaching compassion and giving warmth and meaning to existence. And because the old instinct for order was still alive, she organized this faith and bequeathed it to her foster-children, the nations of western Europe.

So far as science was concerned, Rome held out few inducements to ranging curiosity. Her military activities required surgeons and physicians. Engineers were needed, both for war and peaceful civic services. But the work of such men, if original, was largely empirical. Often it was not original. As so often happens when scientists are ordered to be practical, there was little leeway for the leisurely observation and experiment which are the basis of sound theory. If the knowledge was at hand, ready-made, as in a book of formulae, so much the better. Rome gladly took over what the Greeks knew of medicine, as she pirated, without much subsequent change, the agricultural lore of the Carthaginians. There was no particular stimulus to devise labor-saving mechanisms to the great advantage of physical science as there was in Europe after 1500. In Rome labor was abundant and the problem was to find work for all hands.

The failure to expand greatly the limits of scientific knowledge was no fault of the Roman mind. It was a result of Roman culture, a clear example of what happens to science when the interests of the official state become paramount, and the thoughtful are kept in their place by the practical.

Yet in the long run, Rome rendered inestimable service to science. She furnished, in the Latin tongue, a precise means of communication, and she made possible a common belief for the western world. Since this belief rested heavily on the concept of law and order, spiritual and mundane, it provided the kind of intellectual climate in which science could eventually develop.

There can be no science without accurate, unambiguous symbolism. Many languages do not have this quality. Latin does, for it was forged as an instrument of the art of civilized government. Civil and military leadership both placed high value upon clear, concise expression, and the power and prestige of Rome made her language known throughout the then western world.

The matter of Roman belief, as manifest in the Christian Church, is more involved. The Jewish concept of one universal God and of ordained universal law lost something of its sharpness. Much was made of the miraculous suspension of commonplace natural laws, yet the Church attempted, from time to time, to adjust itself to growing knowledge of the physical universe. The teachings of Christ, based as they were upon the dignity and importance of the individual, focussed more upon soul and the hereafter than upon body, mind, and the present. They tended to discount curiosity about the natural world although they did not prohibit it. And they have, in the course of centuries, certainly tended to encourage a lively concern with body, mind, and the present, so far as these affect human welfare.

Christianity does accept, as contrasted with the thought of the Orient, the importance of the individual. Once this idea is established, the way is open to admit that the individual has a right to use his senses, to form judgments as to reality, and to be heard. It has often been said that Protestantism, by its recognition of individual judgment, contains the seed of its own dissolution. It is not so well understood that the Christian Church, from its very beginning, contained the seeds of Protestantism and of modern science as well.

Beginning with Paul, the doctors of the Christian faith realized that they could not ignore the intellectual problems raised by the Greeks. Even during the slumbering centuries that followed the disintegration of the Roman empire, these problems asserted themselves. Plato, to whom ideas were the only reality, and Aristotle, the naturalist, would not stay decently buried. Within the bosom of the Church itself, the good fathers were far from being in agreement on this issue of the giants.

William of Ockham, in the 14th century, is chiefly remembered for his famous dictum in favor of the simplest explanation possible (*frustra fit per plura quod potest fieri per pauciora*)—an indispensable tool of logic in the formulation of scientific theory. But this was only an incident in his labors. He was almost completely realistic and modern in insisting that ideas are a product of human experience, and that such experience, derived as it is from sense impressions, is the valid basis for thought. This grey friar of Oxford wrote a Magna Carta of the mind and pointed out the path to the discovery of scientific law.

But in the meantime the rule of universal law had been formulated, and officially sanctioned, in a form less stimulating to scientific investigation. The great St. Thomas Aquinas, eminently clear-headed, understood the validity of natural knowledge, but made it subordinate in importance to spiritual knowledge. Establishing the supreme authority of the Church in the latter field, he was content to proclaim that of Aristotle in science. And so the long shadow of the Greeks lingered on, to the days of Darwin, as the divine right of kings survived the barons of Runnymeade until the Stuarts were disposed of.

Presently the Crusades were stirring sluggish Christendom to its depths, reviving interest in other lands and peoples, and in the writings of the past. The Black Death well-nigh depopulated Europe in the 14th century. Toward the end of the century following Ockham began the great era of world exploration, and on its heels came the Reformation, devastating fraternal wars, and once more the plague.

Here was a combination of circumstances that profoundly affected science. The new geography alone was enough to burst the bounds of old knowledge, while east-west navigation necessitated the perfection of chronometers and other physical instruments. The new commerce created an insatiable demand for the products of European industry, which at the same time was facing an acute labor shortage. Means of mechanical production were sorely needed to replace the old handcrafts. Scholarship, including science, was freed from close ecclesiastical supervision in many places, and even where the power of Mother Church remained, her hand was lightened. The discipline visited upon Galileo, while a regrettable page in the history of knowledge, had more to do with his manners than with his findings. An intense and spectacular dramatic episode in the history of freedom of thought, it nevertheless could be almost matched by a dozen incidents in this year of freedom 1949 A.D. in the enlightened world of today.

Actually, the Great Rebirth or Renaissance was so complex, so rich, so surging with the Divinity and the Evil and above all the Vitality of mankind awake that no simple account is possible. Everyone can read his own meanings into it, and with reason.

Paralleling the courses taught today in Protestant colleges on the Reformation, there are courses on the True Reformation within the Church, taught in Roman Catholic institutions. And Humanists, with no commitments on either side, proclaim with equal justice the victories of their own cause during the Rebirth.

There are even differences of judgment as to how modern science got under way during this great movement. There is the simple doctrine of genius as an unpredictable, explosive force in history, although today most advocates of this idea would grant that even genius must have a reasonable opportunity.

There is the doctrine of necessary sequence—The Seven Seals of Science—which holds that there is an inevitable order in which the sciences *must* develop. The series begins with mathematics and moves up the scale of complexity to a climax in the science of society. This scheme might be more convincing if we did not know that great advances had been made in the more complex sciences by men relatively uninterested in, even ignorant of, the simpler, more basic sciences.

A third doctrine, brilliantly expounded under the influence of Marxism, holds that the various special advances in science have been conditioned by economic and social need. Thus mathematics is said to have arisen from the fundamental need to measure space, time, and mass. Physics followed the needs of navigation and mechanical fabrication. Chemistry and biology came in the train of the industrial revolution, for a variety of reasons.

The choice depends upon how one regards science. Is science a coldly All-Seeing Eye, independent of human concerns, viewing everything impersonally? Is it a realm of purely intellectual achievement, with a compulsive internal logic? Is it the practical servant of human needs, moved by something called economic determinism? Pressing needs for the application of science have arisen, almost in a logical sequence. Yet in magnitude and urgency those needs could have been matched in the overpopulated Orient or the disease-ridden tropics. It is not through genius, through logic, or through necessity alone that we must seek to explain man's scientific achievement, but through the whole process called culture. Actually science is a very highly conditioned cultural enterprise, and while culture does channel the efforts of the individual, it is in turn modified by the choices and the actions of individuals. The cultural history of western Europe had set the stage for science, giving genius its play. In the course of its unfolding drama, the time came for Darwin and Darwin was, in his own peculiar way, ready for the time.

A GREAT RIDDLE

IT SEEMS strange that the mild-mannered men who set about naming, sorting, and arranging the kinds of plants and animals on the earth thereby created a revolution.

Classification—the noting of resemblances and differences—is a habit even among the lower animals. It absorbs much of the energy of the growing human being. In a sense it is the basis of all experience. We have not improved much upon Aristotle's saying that classification rests upon our knowledge of three things—substance, quality, and relation. Yet most of us catalog our surroundings in a rougher fashion. We use names, of course, but we take a great deal for granted. We might be content to group together a large worm, a small snake, and even an eel. If we lived by the sea we should probably consider the sponge and coral as forms of seaweed, although both are animals.

With experience our eyes grow sharper. The fancier of dogs, or of roses, learns to note small distinctions which escape the uninitiated. A farmer or buyer of livestock sees in every flock or herd a group of individuals, each with its distinguishing peculiarities. I have guessed (with some knowledge of the matter) that the average farmer, working as he does with plants and animals, knows somewhat fewer than a hundred different kinds of both. Yet his farm, especially if it is hilly, with a wood and a stream, may easily harbor more than a thousand species of living organisms.

Like the traditional farmer, the hunter, woodsman, and simple herb doctor can get along with a homemade knowledge of plants and animals. This may be acute and useful, so far as it goes. But it lacks the systematic, tested, and universal character of the scientific. The rise of commerce, particularly in drugs, and the needs of the explorer, charged to report the products of strange lands, require knowledge that is more profound.

We are on firm historical ground here. Ancient manuscripts, from China through the Mediterranean lands and on to Central America, reveal the interest of early healers in naming, describing, and arranging the forms of life. And the great expeditions, warlike or peaceful, of which we have record, have brought in their wake a renewed interest in this kind of sorting and cataloging. We know, too, that even primitive people, impressed with the diversity of life, have asked themselves, "How did this all come about?"

To bring about the existence of so many forms of living beings was clearly something beyond man's power, and by logical inference, the work of a greater power. It was in effect an act of creation, and for the western world this idea was made explicit, a perfect example of poetic economy, in the opening chapter of Genesis. Thus the idea of special creation became revealed truth, an item of religious dogma. But never let it be forgotten that this idea was also, for a very long time, the most reasonable and simplest explanation possible, in view of the facts as they were known. The doctrine of Special Creation was, for that reason, not merely an article of faith. It was a respectable scientific theory. This doctrine assumed, of course, that each kind of living thing had been created in its known form and had remained constant thereafter. There was nothing in actual human experience to justify any other assumption. The skillful breeder might manipulate the varieties of dog or pigeon, or (as Jacob did with the flocks and herds of Laban) the kinds of cattle, but he could not transmute them into new species. The ideas of special creation and constancy of species were good science for their day. And the religious belief which incorporated these ideas was a sensible religion for its day, if one grants that the function of religion is to make man at home in the kind of universe he believes himself to be living in.

Greek belief, whatever forms it took, did not provide such a ready-made answer. The Greeks were of a lively, curious disposition and felt their own kinship with nature, which they loved and about which they knew a great deal. Among them, in the course of time, arose the idea that the existing forms of life were the result of a slow process of change and development. This idea, to be later called the doctrine of evolution, took several forms, but all were alike in showing that the Greeks had a sense of process, or dynamic activity.

Anaximander, who lived in the 5th century B.C., thought that nature had produced many forms of life which could not survive because they did not meet the conditions into which they were born. But Nature kept on trying, and eliminating, and so successively better forms were preserved.

Somewhat later Democritus, a vigorous advocate of the theory of atoms, and hence attentive to small matters, pointed out that fitness for survival involved the fitness of various bodily structures, and was not merely some vague property of the whole organism. Finally Aristotle, acute observer and clear thinker of the Golden Fourth Century B.C., espoused the cause now known as evolution, and explained it as the operation of a creative inner principle, working toward the perfection of living forms. He believed in the operation of natural law, not being given to the idea of miraculous meddling. But even his profound and realistic knowledge of nature could not rid him of the belief that things visible were the faulty and imperfect expression of invisible realities—the ideas or forms of his teacher Plato. He did, however, conceive of form as being *within* the thing which expressed it, instead of existing apart in some Celestial remoteness.

We shall never know precisely what these ancients thought, how much they knew, or to what extent they based their judgments on what we would now consider evidence. Most of their writings, including those of Aristotle, have come down to us through many copyings and translations. We can be sure that, during a period longer than that which has elapsed since the birth of modern science, the Greeks were honestly trying to get at fundamental truths of nature. And in the course of this effort, they hit amazingly close to the mark. If their inquiries were hampered by many preconceptions, it was not an utter tragedy. For these preconceptions included such ideas as justice and truth, without which the western world would be a sorry place. Indeed, that world, in the waning days of classic paganism, found itself unable to survive without another absolute—that of love.

Perhaps that is why the clear, brave voice of Lucretius was so long muffled. His highest passion was for unity and truth,

> "for what
> More certain than our senses can there be
> Whereby to mark asunder Error and Truth?" he asks.

Again

> "I prove the supreme law of Gods and sky,
> And the primordial germs of things unfold,
> Whence Nature all creates, and multiplies
> And fosters all, and whither she resolves
> Each in the end when each is overthrown."

Religions he despises, while proclaiming his faith in the ultimate order of universal law. Though remembered chiefly for his statement of the atomic theory, he sketches a doctrine of the evolution of the earth and its inhabitants. He clothes the land with verdure before animals emerge from the sea, and he clearly states that the weak and unfit perish, while the fit survive. He describes a succession, if not a progression, of life and discards the idea of fabulous monsters, such as the centaur, whose bodies did not make anatomical sense. And finally, as did Aristotle, he gives an account of the evolution of human society. While we may agree with his great translator, William Ellery Leonard, that "it is not always easy to know just what Lucretius meant," the meaning is clear enough in general. Compared with the warmth of Christian doctrine, the truth he sees seems bleak and cold, despite the richness of his poet's discourse. But though bleak it is brave and honest, and after Lucretius, speculations as to the origin and development of life lay dormant for eighteen centuries.

These speculations were revived in a way that would have delighted Francis Bacon, by the pressure of countless facts that could not be held together in the accepted framework of belief. For the world grew rapidly after 1500, and no existing system of thought, however magnificently conceived, or however well it had worked before, could pretend to encompass the universe much longer. Colloquial names for plants and animals, which had done well enough, became inadequate. The long Latin sentences which took the place of names among the learned were not much better. Need was served by curiosity, and curiosity grew by what it fed upon. An old scholastic game had been to guess which plants were which, according to Galen and Dioscorides. Presently this blew up of its own inflated nonsense. The plants of northwestern Europe were puzzling enough, for the classic masters had been Mediterranean botanists. Now came plants from America, from Africa, from Asia, lands which obviously the masters had not known. The only animal with a single horn on its nose proved to be the Indian rhinoceros, not the unicorn of fable. Reason began to insist on a hearing. Strictly as a practical matter the unknown productions of distant lands had their value in commerce and certainty was essential. Society could no longer keep books on a basis of mythology and guesswork.

The men who took over the task of establishing order were presumably good Christians of their several kinds. Through the 16th and 17th centuries their hands and minds were occupied with sorting, describing, and naming. So far as we know, their suspicions were not aroused by the fact that plants and animals fell into groups with strong family resemblances—such as the legumes, the buttercups, the cats, and the animals with cloven hoofs that chewed the cud. Perhaps these learned doctors kept some thoughts to themselves. We do not know. They did sometimes speak of plant and animal families, but even sages can be a bit loose with words.

The unit of their describing was the species—a unit which

to this day no one has satisfactorily defined. A species might almost be an expression of one of the ideal forms of old Plato. The individuals of a species though not identical were more like each other, to the trained eye, than they were like the individuals of any other species. There was art, as well as science, in this business. And presently it appeared that species could be grouped again, by reason plus intuition, into larger groups called genera, and these in turn into families.

The problem of naming was not easy. The possibility of using two words in unique combination for each species had been suggested. But not until the 18th century was the practice established. There came along an eager young Swedish naturalist, Carl Linne, who would have been Carl Nilsson, and whose son would have been named Carlson had grandfather Nils not stabilized matters by naming the family once and for all after the linden tree. Linné, or Linnaeus, rendered the same service to biology that his ancestor had conferred upon genealogy. Thereafter each organism was to be known by a binomial—the first name that of the genus, the second that of the species. *Linnaea borealis,* the delicate twinflower of the North, a favorite with Linnaeus, illustrates the principle. There is only one genus *Linnaea* in the plant kingdom, and only one *borealis* among its three or four species.

Linné, or Linnaeus, having neatly solved this troublesome bit of technique, proceeded to become one of the world's greatest classifiers, with animals, plants, and minerals as his objects of study.

We have reason to believe that Linnaeus, the son of a Lutheran pastor, was a devout believer in Special Creation. But we know, too, that as life went on he developed a considerable caution in expressing himself on controversial matters. As a precocious savant, he had paid for the jealousy of his elders. Once they seized upon his belief in the sexuality of plants as a means to discredit him. Only the royal friendship saved him from serious difficulty then.

How frankly thereafter he spoke his mind on the origin of species we cannot know. But his sharp eyes detected the variability of species and their frequently overlapping characters. In his later years he stated that the genus represented the original or type creation, from which species had been derived by modification. A naturalist of his experience could scarcely say less and be true to his profession. How much farther he could have gone in the freer atmosphere of France or England we do not know.

If Linnaeus innocently loosened a bit of mortar, it was the French naturalists who began to pry bricks out of the temple of Special Creation. 18th century France was the France of Voltaire, a country which was learning in the hard way that human thought and belief cannot be forever constrained. As a great colonial power, France was naturally interested in the animal and vegetable life from overseas. So were Spain and England. But thought was hooded in Spain, while England had her hands full with very practical matters, as the contest for foreign colonies eventually proved. So it was the French mind which for a time played over the world of nature with the greatest freedom.

Count Buffon, born in 1707 as was Linnaeus, was a less cautious, more imaginative, naturalist. His interests extended beyond classification into the field of comparative anatomy. Impressed by the relationship between various organs of the vertebrate body, he felt certain that there must be some historical explanation. And because the variations in such organs—jaws, teeth, stomach, or forelimbs—are clearly related to use, he suggested that they have arisen through use and disuse. But Buffon was vulnerable. His philosophy soared, but his laboratory work limped. He was the first to encourage young Cuvier who presently became a master anatomist only to turn bitterly against Buffon and defend the idea of Special Creation to his dying day.

The great Cuvier was destined to discredit another imaginative Frenchman, Jean Pierre Lamarck, often called the most tragic figure in 18th century French science. His contemporary Lavoisier at least died swiftly by the guillotine at the peak of a brilliant career, but Lamarck lived on in blindness, neglect, and ridicule. Lamarck, a good scientific workman, was a clean-cut evolutionist. If he had confined himself to demonstrating relationships throughout the living world he might have fared well. But like Buffon, he advocated an explanation which was at the time (and still seems to be) incapable of proof. This was the doctrine of the inheritance of acquired characters. It supposes that the individual, during its lifetime, may acquire characteristics that will be handed on to its descendants.

In England Darwin's grandfather Erasmus, physician, poet, and competent naturalist to boot, had similar ideas and had advanced them even earlier. Being an amateur, he came off better than poor Lamarck, not receiving much abuse from professional sources. Perhaps even in science there is some protection from the code which forbids the fencing master to fight duels. Incidentally, a letter from Erasmus Darwin to Sir Joseph Banks gives an insight into the minds of these old naturalists who had been brought up in the Christian tradition and were struggling to make sense out of the new flood of facts. "I have no excuse . . . but the knowledge of your general love of science, and your philanthropy to wish that science to be propagated amongst your countrymen."

An even more famous amateur of natural history was another poet, Goethe, who joined the evolutionists, with his doctrine of Metamorphosis. By means of his own charming pictures, he showed that flower parts are but altered leaves, a principle which still commands respect among plant anatomists. Thus evolution no less than religion had its poets—Lucretius, Darwin, Goethe, and later, Tennyson. And why not? There is emotional grandeur in the idea of evolution. It is not a sordid and inhumane doctrine.

The roster of the early 1800's listed some impressive critics of the idea of instant, miraculous creation. But it had its great defenders, too. Probably the most formidable member of the Old Guard was also the greatest authority on animal structure—Cuvier. He knew the anatomy of animals, extinct as well as living. The Baron has probably been misrepresented by both friend and foe, and certainly has been blamed for some of the statements of his more enthusiastic followers. He seems to have believed that animals of the past had been killed off by more or less spectacular cataclysms, and new forms created to take their place. As a scientist he was not satisfied with the evidence *against* Special Creation, and we cannot blame him for that. But we can blame him for not being tolerant of those who were searching for a more rational explanation.

Stimulated by the new search for mineral wealth, and also by genuine curiosity, the geologists of the early 1800's were already beginning to question the idea of a miraculous and supernatural past. To their opened eyes, the present revealed marvels enough in the way of a dynamic universe. Under such leaders as Hutton, Geikie, and Lyell, they began to see that existing rocks and land forms were explainable in terms of processes which are in operation today. Once this idea, called Uniformitarianism, was adopted and put to work, it proved itself a powerful and dependable instrument for making sense out of what had been geological confusion.

The older naturalists did not exactly ignore environment. They knew that drouth, untimely frost, or lack of air could destroy living organisms. But there was, and is, so much to be learned about each living creature that we may pardon these men for expecting too complete an answer from a study of plants and animals apart from environment. Chemists and physicists were already making such an approach untenable. They had shown that every breath represents an interchange of material between animal and environment, and that most of the solid material in plants comes from the invisible atmosphere. Working with instruments of precision, they were demonstrating that these processes were quantitatively exact and qualitatively binding. Neither the king on his throne, nor the snail in the garden, nor any other living thing was exempt from the operation of physical principles. The day was at hand when no philosophy of life could presume to ignore the ceaseless operation of environment.

Nor could this environment longer be regarded as the unpredictable plaything of some supernatural wrath or pleasure. Henceforth man must face the chilling, but by no means hopeless, challenge of making his way through an understanding of universal laws, and of controlling himself with respect to the operation of these laws. Ethics were not to be abolished, but rather to be set up in a new system of coordinates. In theological language, the Will of God was to be seen as something far grander, far less trivial, than men had dreamed. If God himself were the more inscrutable, His ways at least were plainer, and open for all to see.

This is not to say that the ways of the universe are self-evident, or always easy to interpret. The natural environment is enormously complicated, for it includes not merely the inanimate physical world, but all living organisms and thus man himself. As early as 1751, the wise Benjamin Franklin had given thought to this matter. Allowing for all the shiploads of men and women that had come to the American Colonies from Europe, the increase in white population in America had been stupendous. Franklin saw that here was a general principle of nature. "There is, in short, no bound to the prolific nature of plants or animals, but what is made by their crowding and interfering with each other's means of subsistence." This in itself was a breach in the wall between moral and natural knowledge, a breach now grown to mighty proportions. And yet, two centuries later, only a small minority of mankind concedes that Franklin's dictum applies to our own species. Man has an exemption, mystical in the eyes of some and practical in the eyes of others, through his own cleverness in discovery and fabrication.

Franklin died in 1790. Eight years later Thomas Malthus printed his *Essay on Population,* a sober warning to those who believed that Utopia was just around the bend of the road. Using the same basic idea that Franklin had advanced, he showed that, unless man restricts his own rate of increase, war, disease, and hunger will intervene to check it. Malthus, who had been ordained an Anglican priest but was teaching political economy, knew he was playing with dynamite. His first edition was anonymous. The cautious revisions which came later show that he was a worried man. The issue which he raised is as current and lively today as it was in his lifetime. The sources of his opposition are formidable and the character of its arguments are amazing. But the important thing is that, in explicit fashion, he showed a natural mechanism whereby populations may be restrained from moving toward infinite multitude and intolerable crowding.

Erasmus Darwin read and understood the tract, and so, in due time, did his grandson. To each in turn came vision. For the grandson this vision led to years of patient, plodding toil in search of countless bits of evidence from which he at last could build a mighty structure of principle.

YOUNG MAN AT SEA

THERE is a curious parallel between young Charles Darwin and Tom Sawyer. To see this, we must transpose the setting from a midwestern American cottage to a dignified English country home. We must shift from the unruly Mississippi to the placid Severn. And—most difficult of all—we must be able to see Huck Finn in the several persons of shooting companions, young fellow naturalists, and the few science professors whose presence in classical Cambridge was tolerated at the time. Like Tom, Darwin grew up in two worlds that had little in the way of a bridge between. For both, the prescribed activities of home and school could not match in interest the adventure out-of-doors. The English boy's boon companions were far from ragged or disreputable, but it was feared for a time that their influence and his own tastes would lead him to become nothing better than "an idle shooting fellow." And the contrast between his inclinations and those which his family approved led him to become, for a long time, a sadly bewildered young man.

Yet Darwin's great service to mankind was the outcome of his very doubt, uncertainty, and suspended judgment. His lifework was to have a curiously fumbling character, misunderstood by men not reared in the discipline of science, but clear and reasonable enough to those who have been. It was to be predicated on a quality almost contemptible in the eyes of certain serene idealists—the capacity to change one's mind in the face of new physical realities.

There was an element of confusion in Darwin's inheritance. One grandfather was a gentleman, physician, and extrovert poet.

The other was a craftsman potter who achieved wealth and greatness for himself and who thereby, under the admirable flexibility of the English system, achieved social position for his sons and daughters. Darwin's mother, Susannah Wedgwood, whom he barely remembered, was a Unitarian. Her people had made the break with revealed religion. His father, Dr. Robert Darwin, was solid Church of England and into this faith, with its then acceptance of the literal scripture, Charles was baptized.

True, not all of the elements in the background were discordant. The love of plants and an interest in gardening were then, as now, almost universal in rural England. The same may be said about enthusiasm for animals, whether wild or domestic. The horse was the chief means of overland travel, and dogs, of course, were indispensable in hunting and shooting. Gentlemanly devotion to natural history was acceptable among folks of means and leisure, likewise an even warmer zeal for the sports of field and stream. Integrity, courage, and dogged perseverance were socially esteemed and in the whole family tradition. So was public service, within the limits of definite conventions.

It is more than likely that the fused heritage of potter and poet had much to do with Darwin's intuitive sense of form. For form as a clue to organization was the gateway through which Charles approached the study of nature. Not that he was an artist. But landscapes, organisms, and populations had to make sense to him in terms of structure and history, or he was not content.

His temperament was warm, spontaneous, and lovable, finding more outlet at the informal and comfortable home of his Uncle Josiah Wedgwood than in his father's somewhat austere establishment. There seems to be no question of his father's dominating personality, nor of Charles' apprehensive feelings toward an older sister who managed him as well as the rest of the household. His brother Erasmus, five years his senior, had a good mind and an excellent education, but never sought any career beyond living on his inherited means, and Charles always felt sorry for him.

Formal schooling was a protracted ordeal for young Charles.

He later regarded it as a dead loss on two counts. The teaching was bad and the tight classical curriculum gave no play to his abounding curiosity. At eight he went for a year to a day-school, then for seven years to a grammar-school at Shrewsbury, whose headmaster one day reproved him for wasting time in chemical experiments with his brother Erasmus. But there is no sign that, for all his disgust and sense of futility, he ever became morbid or lapsed into self-pity. He was made of sturdier stuff. And he found increasing solace in his collections of minerals and insects and in his shooting at the Wedgwood estate.

At sixteen he went up to Edinburgh to study medicine, joining his brother there. This, too, proved a dreary academic venture, the teaching, in his judgment, being intolerably bad. But he found congenial interests outside of the curriculum among fellow-naturalists. Here he presented his first scientific observations and began to judge men and facts. He walked out on Audubon when that smart Frenchman criticized a scientist whom Darwin respected. He made mistakes, too—the most serious being his neglect of practical work in dissection and anatomy. Such training would have been extremely useful to him in later years.

The Edinburgh adventure and the vocation to medicine ended within two years. Anaesthetics were unknown at the time, and the nightmare of watching operations performed on conscious patients was too much for this sensitive and sympathetic young Englishman whose life was presently to become almost a continual display of courage and staying power.

Father Darwin was paying the bills. He was also making the decisions. If medicine was out, the Church was in, and Charles must go up to Cambridge to fit himself for the ministry of the Church of England. The whole business seems to have been quite matter-of-fact. There were no anguished soul-searchings as there might have been had Charles been headed for the celibate Catholic priesthood or the vigorous evangelism of the Nonconformists. We note, too, the absence of any serious intellectual misgivings on the part of this young naturalist, student of the physical world. He wondered a bit about the creed, but by his own testimony, the fundamental questions of the universe were at that time taken care of for him in Holy Scripture, and it never occurred to him to doubt the literal truth of Genesis.

Entering Christ's College in the autumn of 1827, Darwin emerged with a pass B.A. in the spring of 1831. So far as academic work was concerned, he considered this a period of wasted time, with classics, mathematics, and moral philosophy as the main subjects of formal instruction. A half century later, William Bateson found the mathematics teaching at Cambridge uninspiring. He confessed that he might have become greatly interested if this subject had been as cleverly taught as it is today.

Yet Darwin, with good reason, looked back on the years at Cambridge as his happiest. He became one of a group of mildly roistering young sportsmen, companions who furnished an effective antidote for his dull and distasteful class work. He collected beetles with a true British passion, read geology, and learned a good deal of botany from Professor Henslow in off hours. His friends included a number of excellent naturalists, and several men who were his seniors. It is safe to say that he learned as much on his own as an American college student, working his way, ordinarily gets from class instruction. British higher education is still superior to that in America in its tradition of independent study. The young Englishman thinks nothing of "getting up," through systematic reading and conversation, a subject on which his American cousin must "have a course" or remain ignorant.

Following this tradition, young Darwin, who had never taken a course in geology, spent part of the summer of 1831 with Professor Sedgwick, doing geological field work in Wales. At the end of August, through the interest of his friend, Professor Henslow, he received an offer to sail as naturalist on board the naval ship *Beagle,* bound for a lengthy survey trip in the southern hemisphere. The appointment carried no salary, and entailed some expense. It also meant postponement of Holy Orders.

The 22-year-old lad had to secure his father's permission. This was at first refused. But Uncle Josiah Wedgwood, the potter's practical and sensible son, intervened and the coveted blessing was obtained. This venture into science was regarded by all concerned as a gentlemanly avocation which would not interfere too much with a serious future profession. A clergyman naturalist to whom the post had been previously offered felt it would not be quite sporting to absent himself from his two "livings" for the period of the voyage. Charles was in no such box, as yet. He never did renounce his intention to become a priest, but as he put it later, the idea died a natural death on the *Beagle* expedition.

The voyage belongs to history. It began late in December, 1831, and ended in October, 1836, thus lasting five years instead of the two originally planned. Darwin's account of it, a classic in its own right, was to give him more sheer pleasure than any of his other writings. As to the experience itself, we have his testimony.

> "The voyage of the 'Beagle' has been by far the most important event in my life, and has determined my whole career; yet it depended on so small a circumstance as my uncle offering to drive me thirty miles to Shrewsbury [to overcome parental objection], which few uncles would have done, and on such a trifle as the shape of my nose. [Capt. Fitz-Roy, who fancied himself as a physiognomist, feared that no man with a nose like Darwin's could possibly have stamina for such an adventure.] I have always felt that I owe to the voyage the first real training or education of my mind."

Physically, however, the experience was a severe ordeal. Darwin suffered greatly from seasickness, and no doubt from improper diet, although the captain stocked scurvy-preventing foods. Space was severely limited, and so the young naturalist was forced to keep his gear and quarters in trim shape. His specimens were a different matter, often being spread out for drying or study to the great disgust of his shipmates. Since the party was mainly engaged in a survey of the South American coast, there were numerous opportunities for field trips on that continent, some of them for considerable distances overland. Frequent letters and shipments of collected materials back to England, as well as a detailed journal and notebooks, give us a thorough record of the whole experience.

When Darwin sailed from England, he was a confident believer in the "Mosaic" account of creation and apparently accepted Archbishop Usher's decision that the earth dated from 4004 B.C. He was a skilled observer and competent collector, although not a disciplined biologist. He already knew the techniques of geological observation and mapping. In his kit was Lyell's new *Principles of Geology,* whose main theme, following Hutton, was uniformity—the idea that the processes which were shaping the earth today were the same as those which had operated throughout its history.

Darwin had also certainly read his grandfather's *Zoonomia,* a poetic account of the evolution of life. It had interested him, but seems to have struck no spark at the time. Doubtless it lay in his subconscious until there had accumulated an explosive mixture of facts that strained the doctrine of Special Creation to the bursting point. If the delayed fuse of his grandfather's ideas actually set off the fireworks, there is no evidence that he realized it, then or later. He gave the credit to Malthus.

His captain, whose paying guest and messmate he was, was a nephew of Lord Castlereagh, a gentleman and sailor to his fingertips. Capt. Fitz-Roy was also profoundly religious and a literal believer. Both he and Darwin were youngsters of spirit, and it is more than likely that the sailor's rigid beliefs, contrasting so vividly with the growing evidence before Darwin's eyes, sharpened the latter's thoughts into a new keenness and precision. Inevitably Fitz-Roy's mind became the whetstone, Darwin's the knife.

The coast of South America, with its great rivers and recently elevated layers of sedimentary rocks, many of them full of fossils, was an open book of dynamic process. So were the mountains, the lava beds, islands and, later, the coral formations of tropical waters. All of these Darwin did his best to map and describe, and his geological work was professional in its quality.

But description was not enough. The same insistent urge which, as we know, had moved Erasmus and Robert before him, the urge to get at a workable theory or explanation, gave the mind of Charles no rest. The doctrine of uniformity, of gradual orderly change, had been developed in the neatly ordered geological confines of western Europe. Darwin put it to work in an interpretation of a vast, geologically unknown and varied continent.

Somewhere along the crooked coastline Bishop Usher's date of Creation silently vanished as an even remotely conceivable truth. The serious young Englishman, facing the massive reality of the ages, could not be burdened with such nonsense. This lanky, dogged, troubled, seasick boy was about to set a stage, uncramped in space or time, for a magnificent reconstruction of the pageant of terrestrial life. It was a great moment in the history of human thought.

Along with the rocks and fossils, Darwin was studying living plants and animals, observing their behavior and distribution, collecting, drying, pickling, and describing. At every convenient port, bales and barrels of specimens, and sheafs of notes went back to England. The task he attempted—and accomplished—seems overwhelming to a modern biologist, who would scarcely tackle such an expedition today without a staff of specialists. The thing that saved young Darwin was his self-control. In the midst of bewildering scientific richness, he stuck stoutly to his belief that fewer specimens, well-annotated and preserved, were of more use than a multitude swept into the net without proper care.

Professor Henslow had told him, in discussing the voyage, that he was not a finished naturalist, and this was true. But he could see and think, and was a tireless worker. His knowledge of plant and animal classification, and of comparative anatomy, was meager by the standards of Cuvier, Huxley, and Agassiz. Yet he caught what Huxley missed, and what the two other masters stoutly refused to acknowledge.

Perhaps his case is parallel to that of Priestley, who said that, had he been trained as a chemist, he never would have discovered oxygen. The innocent eye has its advantages, as every artist knows to his profit, and every sleight-of-hand performer to his grief.

To any man with intuitive scientific gifts, seeing is the first step towards believing. Darwin saw for himself the unbelievable richness of tropical life, with its myriads of forms all so admirably suited to the general temperature conditions of the tropics, yet each form so marvelously fitted to the particular niche which it occupied in the economy of nature. Noah's Ark, so confidently and minutely pictured in a publication of the Clarendon Press at Oxford, under the date of 1801, must have begun to seem pitifully inadequate, and any conceivable Garden of Eden in Asia Minor or instant fiat out of the question in accounting for the origin of the plants of this remote continent of South America.

But the thing which really upset the neat old system was the inescapable fact that no species (except man and his dog) was universal. Each kind of living thing seemed limited to its peculiar range, and to have its nearest kin nearest at hand. Differences increased, among related forms, with distance, just as they should if relationship were correspondingly more remote. This phenomenon, first suggested on the continent of South America, became clearer as the islands of the Pacific were visited, until it burst upon the consciousness of young Darwin that here was a problem whose answer was not ready-made by authority. Instead, it was a fair challenge to his energy and his wits, as honest and as free as the problem of the chemistry of the atmosphere had been to Priestley, Lavoisier, and Scheele, more than fifty years before. From that day forward, his efforts were devoted to the problem of species. And in the due course of time, he became convinced that species are not immutable creations that have lasted, in their present form, since the beginnings of the world.

The five-year voyage ended, he returned to England and settled down to the analysis and publication of his results. The geological reports were distinguished on their merits. The biological findings were competent, no more than that, but Darwin's place in the fraternity of scientists became assured. In 1839 he married his first cousin Emma, daughter of his Uncle Josiah

Wedgwood, and in 1842 moved to Down in Kent. There he passed the remainder of his life, under handicaps of ill health that would have overwhelmed most men.

Insistently, the problem of species and their origin haunted his mind. As early as 1837 he had begun to keep notes on this subject, collecting facts, reflecting upon them, and, in the faithful tradition of the Darwin family for at least three generations, trying to shape theories to account for them. It is clear that one experience gave direction to his thought. In 1838 he read by chance, as one today might pick up a detective story or a novel, the treatise on population written by Malthus. (See p. 25) His mind was ripe and ready for what he read in that famous discourse. In the tropics he had seen the immense fertility of nature in producing living organisms, and the terrific mortality which eliminated all but the relatively few which survived to maturity. But until this moment the observation had not really registered—an ironical but frequent experience which almost every working scientist can match from his own record.

The whole art of agriculture and livestock growing, from its beginnings in Neolithic time, is based on the deliberate control of populations of plants and animals. Castration has been called, properly enough, one of the earliest and greatest of man's biological inventions. Yet because the farmer and herdsman think always in terms of increase, men until the days of Franklin and Malthus were blind to the underlying principle of constantly effective restriction, or elimination, in their own operations. When it came to organisms in nature, the obscurity was even greater. Malthus' suggestion that it applied even to man's own exalted species—though that species had practiced infanticide for ages—was, and still is in many circles, simply too much.

Darwin opened his notebook on the species problem in July of 1837. He read Malthus in October of the following year, fifteen months later. In his own words, "being well prepared to appreciate the struggle for existence which everywhere goes on, from long-continued observation of the habits of plants and animals, it at once struck me that under these circumstances favorable variations would tend to be preserved, and unfavorable ones destroyed. The result of this would be the formation of new species." Here at length was a dynamic process, clearly operating throughout the world of nature, and a possible key to his riddle of the origin of species.

Four years later, in 1842, he was ready to draft a first sketch of his theory of the origin of species by the survival of the fittest in the struggle for existence through natural selection. In 1844 he developed a more complete statement. His scientific intimates, Lyell and Hooker, were taken into his confidence, so that they knew what he was doing during the next fourteen years which he spent in the painful accumulation of further evidence.

Meanwhile another Englishman, Alfred Russel Wallace, who had begun the practice of natural history—collecting and studying—in the tropics in 1848, had worked out an explanation quite the same as Darwin's. As with Darwin, the key had been supplied by a reading of Malthus. In 1858 he sent his manuscript to Darwin for criticism, and to be shown to Lyell. Darwin saw that he had been scooped. But he had that quaint old-fashioned quality called "Honour" and so, as a matter of course, he proposed to Lyell that Wallace's manuscript be submitted for publication. Lyell and Hooker ruled otherwise, insisting that "in the interests of science generally" both papers be presented together—a double charge of intellectual dynamite which left the audience reeling.

The thesis was simplicity itself. No two organisms are precisely alike. The powers of reproduction far exceed the capacity of the earth to sustain the organisms produced. Relentlessly and inevitably many must perish, few survive. By a process as impersonal as the law of gravity there is a natural selection of those which—by their favorable qualities—are best fitted to survive. Those unfitted are eliminated at once, along with a large proportion of those whose fitness is indifferently good. The fittest which survive and reproduce transmit their characteristics.

Here at length was a natural mechanism, plausible and consistent, which might explain the amazing and intricate adjustments of surviving species to their conditions of life. Darwin admitted that the cause of variation he could not explain, but he foresaw the rich scientific possibilities of this problem. He has been criticized for coming to believe that the law of natural selection is a fundamental law of the universe, as the law of gravity is. Strict modern analysis may construe it as a corollary of other principles, such as those of modern genetics, the law of limiting factors, and the principles of thermodynamics. But only a hardy soul would venture in our present stage of human experience to say that any principle of science, however broad its scope, is primary and not derivative.

Darwin had stated a thesis which was reasonably adequate. which fitted the known facts. He had accumulated a vast body of data consistent with his thesis. Difficulties he saw, and readily admitted. There is no evidence that he suppressed any inconvenient arguments against his point of view. And if, in a sense, he became advocate as well as investigator, he observed the principle of Sir Rufus Isaacs, who used to say that he won his cases by "deadly fair play."

Within a year after the reading of his paper and that of Wallace, he tossed the issue beyond the restricted walls of the citadel of science into the turbulent stream of general human thought. The first edition of his book, *The Origin of Species,* was sold out within a day. The fat was in the fire, but it was not Darwin's fat that was to be consumed.

HIGH EXPLOSIVE

IMAGINE two giant firecrackers suddenly exploded in a roomful of peaceful knitters in rocking chairs, with only two of them in on the prank. You will have some measure of the effect produced by the reading of Darwin's paper, along with that of Wallace's, at the Linnean Society on the memorable 1st of July, 1859. Joseph Hooker, the botanist, and Charles Lyell, equally famous geologist, knew what was coming. The others did not, and were the further stunned when Hooker and Lyell got up to approve the audacity to which they had been subjected. In Hooker's words "the interest excited was intense, but the subject was too novel and too ominous for the old school to enter the lists before armouring."

In November of the next year the first edition of Darwin's book *The Origin of Species by Natural Selection* appeared, and this edition of 1250 copies was immediately bought up. A formidable work by ordinary standards, and well fortified with data, it was nevertheless regarded by Darwin as an abstract. Considering the immensity of the subject, he was correct. The text was continuously modified and expanded in succeeding editions. Indeed the bulk of biological research and thought since its appearance has been a continuing revision, expansion, and critique of Darwin's thesis.

Allowing as we must for the limitations of technical knowledge at the time, the book remains a solid piece of architecture. It still stands rugged, though waves of attack upon its honesty, its logic, and its scientific competence have dashed against it. This is not to call it infallible, but rather to proclaim its essential greatness. There are no finalities in science, only the capacity for growth. The *Origin of Species* meets this proper measure of its quality.

The book begins with an account of the variations that have occurred in domesticated animals and plants, under the eye and guidance of man, then proceeds to discuss those that are known to have occurred in nature. Variability and change it shows to be the rule throughout the realm of living things.

Next comes evidence of the all-pervading struggle to remain alive and reproduce. This chapter reviews the tremendous capacity of organisms to increase in comparison with their limited capacity to survive. The idea, of course, came from Malthus, and should be patent to anyone who can count seeds and seedlings, eggs and fish, or who can read vital statistics of the human race. Yet by some perversity, it is still disputed by otherwise intelligent and well-informed people.

Then follows the clinching—and controversial—thesis, under the title of "natural selection." Within a year, replying to searching comments of W. H. Harvey, Darwin came to admit that he might better have used the term "natural preservation," since the term "selection" implies conscious or deliberate action. He had, of course, been led to use the term because the results of human selection in animal and plant breeding were so apposite to the processes of nature. In later years Alfred Russel Wallace in a most lucid and trenchant piece of scientific correspondence reenforced the criticism of Harvey, but by that time the mold had set.

The point of natural selection is that the environment—the whole set of living conditions—acts as a screen or sieve. Organisms which, so to speak, fit the mesh can survive and reproduce. Those which do not fit are eliminated. In this sense it is the fittest which persist and so in later editions, Darwin added Spencer's phrase "survival of the fittest."

Now elimination of the unfit is a negative process, not a creative one. Peculiar and highly specialized fitness must be explained, and the keenest of Darwin's critics levelled their fire upon this point, often overlooking his simple explanation that there is an unlimited tendency to variation in nature, thus affording constantly new opportunities for increasing fitness. The causes of variation, he frankly admitted that he did not know. "Our ignorance of the laws of variation is profound" is his conclusion at the end of his chapter on those laws. This chapter, together with a later one on hybridism, are scientifically obsolete today, yet of the greatest historical importance. The ignorance which he confesses persisted until a generation after his passing. Yet he shrewdly predicted that a study of variation would open a "grand and hitherto untrodden field of investigation."

After considering variation, the book proceeds to deal with difficulties and objections to the theory of natural selection, in a spirit of candor which has never been seriously doubted. It next deals with the troublesome problem of behavior, specifically, instinct, as a factor in natural selection. Then, following the chapter on hybridism above referred to, it considers the geological record and the facts of geographical distribution—two fields which have continued to yield overwhelming evidence of the *reality* of evolution, and considerable evidence as to the *character of the process.*

Finally, there is a discussion of the evident degrees of relationships among existing plants and animals, as revealed by similarities and differences in bodily structure and development. Curiously enough, although some of the most violent attacks were to be levelled against Darwin by specialists on anatomy, their own work ultimately provided some of the deadliest ammunition used by the Darwinians in his defense.

The *Origin of Species* ends tidily, as does each chapter, with a summary and conclusions.

Darwin had not originated the idea of evolution. That idea was the expression of a long and dignified history of thought. Others had preceded him in at least brief statements of the idea of natural selection, and Wallace had developed it independently. In every one of the several disciplines of scientific knowledge there were contemporaries who excelled Darwin in professional training and specialized learning. Some of Darwin's evidence is wrong, and more was, through no fault of his, insufficiently verified. He shifted his position on some matters as time went on. In the end, although he neglected Buffon, he became more tolerant of Lamarck, and might eventually have come to appreciate even his own grandfather!

Yet the fact remains that he brought the problem of evolution into clearer focus than anyone ever had, piled up more, and more pertinent, evidence on the subject, and for the first time offered a reasonable, not to say plausible, explanation for the process. Therein lay his prodigious, solid achievement, and the perennial cry "Darwinism Discredited!" does not touch the essence of the matter.

The battle of the giants which followed publication has been often described, and forms one of the most diverting chapters in the history of science. Nor was the melee confined to giants—midgets kept darting in between their legs to add to the entertainment. Generally speaking, the small men who opposed Darwinism have had a better press than those extremists, the neo-Darwinians, who, with dim understanding and narrow conceptions, have fanatically supported it, which is just as well.

There is no point in repeating here the chronicle of debate, tempting as that prospect is. Instead, let us examine the general credentials of the groups who took an active part. This is a somewhat dangerous procedure, yet useful. The more closely one looks at the record of proponent and opponent, the more evident becomes the influence of temperament, personal experience, and intuitive belief, all subtly blending themselves with professional judgment. There can be no more striking evidence that science—so commonly assumed to be operating in an atmosphere of complete detachment, almost in a cultural vacuum—is in reality a highly conditioned cultural enterprise.

The small cordon which formed the intimate nucleus in favor of Darwinism consisted of men who, with the possible exception of Huxley, were primarily men of the field rather than the laboratory. This was certainly true of Darwin and Wallace. It was equally true of the great botanists, Hooker in England and Gray in America. Although both of the latter spent most of their time in the herbarium, each was a notable collector, with a wide-ranging experience of living plants in their natural environments.

Lyell, who with Hooker had stood by Darwin during the slow course of his developing idea, was preeminently a field geologist, notable for his extensive travels and first-hand knowledge of conditions in the field. There is a good example of this and a charming glimpse of Lyell's mind in the two small volumes which chronicle his second visit to the United States. His writing as well as that of Gray, Hooker, and Huxley, has an atmosphere of dateless, universal discourse which marks the true classic.

Huxley in England, and Gegenbauer and Haeckel in Germany, are probably to be considered as primarily laboratory scientists. Yet each began his career with field-work, the two Germans in the Mediterranean, and Huxley as a ship's surgeon on H.M.S. *Rattlesnake*. Of the three instances, that of Gegenbauer is probably least complex. He appears to have been moved, in his support of evolution, by the cool facts of comparative anatomy. Unlike many of his co-workers in that field, he was able to free himself from the overwhelming influence of Cuvier.

Haeckel's grasp of the problems of living nature is suggested by the fact that he coined the word "oecology," now "ecology," to cover the study of the broad configurations which exist within and among communities of organisms. Neither he nor Huxley stood in awe of authority or the established order, social or intellectual. Both were controversialists, but of very different types. Haeckel was bitter and ultimately, in the opinion of most scientists, he went off center. Huxley fought with a smile seldom distant. With the possible exception of his last public address, there is little harshness from his lips or pen. Unlike Haeckel, his intelligence was too finely poised, his imagination too sensitive, to permit him to become doctrinaire. And he had that superb quality without which morphology is blind and stupid—an intuitive sense of form. Of this his literary style is proof.

The scientists who opposed Darwin were a mixed lot, but included some highly competent individuals. There were those who refused to accept any kind of evolution, preferring to believe in Special Creation. Others believed in some measure of organic transformation, interspersed with cataclysms, repeated creations, or spontaneous generation, according to their particular faith or lack of it. Still others were convinced evolutionists, some denying the operation of natural selection as an agent in evolution. Others admitted its existence, but were inclined to see limits to its effectiveness. Of this last-named group of critics, perhaps the most acute were those who saw in it a negative principle and were unwilling to concede it any constructive role.

Not the least spectacular opponent of Darwin was Louis Agassiz, Swiss-born zoologist and Harvard colleague of Asa Gray, and one of the most accomplished naturalists of his day. That he had an original, even bold, mentality is shown by his proof of continental glaciation.[1] Yet he would not accept the doctrine of evolution. There is a legend of the laboratory backstairs that, on his death-bed, he admitted this to have been a professional mistake. In his youth he had for a time been close to Cuvier. He was also, like many of the young continental scientists of his day, tinged with the romantic naturalism to which Goethe had given his blessing.

Springing from 18th century natural philosophy, and with a lineage back to the idealism of Plato, romantic naturalism was more like its shaggy, undisciplined parent than its austere remote ancestor. But, like both, it regarded ideas as the reality, and what most of us call reality it regarded as their imperfect reflection. To its followers evolution was no problem. Do not ideas show varying degrees of difference and resemblance? What

[1] But see Flint, R. F., *Glacial Geology and the Pleistocene Epoch,* pp. 2–5. Wiley. 1947.

more natural than that their clumsy material expressions—the forms of life—should do likewise? To turn from discourse such as this to the lucid writing of Asa Gray is like moving from a muddy brook to a limpid spring. For Gray would seem as reasonable to a Greek, or, I venture, to one of our descendants ten centuries from now as he does to us. Gray asserted his belief in a personal God, but the relationship was one of high dignity where neither he nor his God presumed to put words into the mouth of the other.

In fairness to Agassiz—and he deserves the greatest generosity, for he was generous—it should be said that he did not confine himself to *a priori* reasoning, but also stated reasonable scientific objections. He called for evidence of the plasticity of species—which we now have. He also called for something more constructive than natural selection, a creative, dynamic, driving force within life itself. On this last point he had, and today has, distinguished company. He was not too completely apart from Darwin himself in that respect, if we allow for the characteristic caution with which Darwin dealt with the mysterious problem of variation.

The rich orchestration of Agassiz's ideas compasses the range of professional criticism, notably in Germany. There was Kölliker, for example. In a mood of the highest respect for Darwin's sincerity and scientific craftsmanship, and with a frank rejection of the doctrine of Special Creation, he confined his objections to matters within the competence of science to investigate.

French scientists gave the *Origin* a cool reception. A number of them took it in their stride, as a valid scientific contribution, and proceeded quietly about their business. Disciples of Cuvier and Lamarck were not amused, let alone convinced. Nor were there lacking sharp Gallic minds, trained both in biology and dialectic, to point out possible weaknesses in Darwin's armor.

To return to England, it has often been said that the trend toward individualism and laissez faire in social, economic, and political thought had made the time overripe for an uncritical acceptance of Darwinism in secular, lay circles. Certainly Herbert Spencer had announced his belief in evolution while Darwin was still at work on his notebooks, and later came out as a champion for natural selection, coining the not too happy phrase "survival of the fittest," which Darwin subsequently adopted.

The use of this phrase, the idea of ruthless struggle for existence, and the unquestionably sordid industrial and financial developments of the 19th century have made it rather a fashion to intimate that Darwinism served as a convenient excuse for evil. Evangelical Protestantism had relaxed the old churchly authority over economic life, giving greater emphasis to religion as an individual, rather than a social concern. Business practices which would have drawn the wrath of the medieval church came to be viewed with tolerance. But this situation long antedated Darwin, and he is scarcely to be blamed for it.

In the long perspective of Anglo-Saxon struggle for human rights there is something brighter than utter ruthlessness. The road from slavery to freedom is a toilsome way. The greater part of mankind still struggles along its early and its middle reaches. Its segments must first be charted, then slowly traversed. First comes the hurdle of spiritual worth of the individual, and after it in confused succession the barriers to his freedom of thought and speech, to political expression, and to economic justice. The economic and legal privileges of the individual, while still being won, were inadvertently and for convenience transferred to corporations whose future strength could not be guessed. This has slowed the forward movement of human rights. But it is not a turning back, merely an obstacle in the way, to be removed as others before it have been. The future will see that the 19th century was a continuing march toward freedom, not a retreat into slavery.

Spectacular as was the impact of the evolution doctrine upon the technical fields of biological and social thought, both had been committed to the reception and testing of new ideas. It was the recognized business of scholars in both fields, after the initial excitement—even indignation—to get down to business and look for evidence wherever the search might lead them.

In the field of religion the problem was vastly more complicated. Few forms of faith, with such notable exceptions as the Friends, the Unitarians, and perhaps the Zoroastrians, have been content to make a minimum of assumptions. It is the inquiring mind, not the devout, which has followed the counsel of Ockham, *"causa non sunt multiplicanda praeter necessitatem."* (Explanations are not to be multiplied beyond the requirements.) Or perhaps it is fairer to say, because religion does deal with matters of such tremendous importance, that its prophets and fathers conceive the necessities to be vast, and on that basis expand the range of deduction and corollary.

At any rate, an individual wishing to profess the Fatherhood of God, the Brotherhood of Man, and perhaps the Love of Christ, and to find fellowship with others of like mind, has generally been expected to pledge himself to a whole body of contingent belief and practice. Sometimes, as in early Victorian England, the range of choice among such bodies of religious thought was not too free. And the tension was gathering.

Darwin had been reared in an unquestioning belief that the poetic account of creation in Genesis was literal truth. His life exemplified the Christian virtues and a belief in the dignity of the individual. The institutional religion of his day offered the choice of both salvation and literal belief, or neither. Karl Pearson speaks of the "dogmatic teaching which was impressed upon the pre-Darwinian child." And again, of the way in which the "Mosaic fetters ate into and cankered the very spirit of scientific investigation."

The noble Galton, writing to Darwin in 1869, had this to say: "I used to be wretched under the weight of the old-fashioned 'argument from design' of which I felt although I was unable to prove to myself the worthlessness . . . your book drove away the constraint of my old superstition as if it had been a nightmare and was the first to give me freedom of thought." Galton lived to confirm this declaration in a public address in 1908.

Outside the field of science, professional guardians of dogmatic faith sprang up and waved their arms at the evolutionists as though a catch had been released on that fateful 25th of November, 1859. Plausible, disingenuous, and ill-informed, Bishop Wilberforce of the Church of England led with his chin to Huxley, as we have noted in the preface to this book. Even his clerical supporters were ashamed of him and by 1880 the issue had boiled itself away among serious thinkers of the Episcopal persuasion. Cardinal Manning lashed out in white fury, with some dignity and style, true, but with scant attention to the other side of the argument.

Thus under interdict as they were at first, the evolutionists presently found that a good chaplain had joined their growing regiment. Lovable, wise, and witty, Charles Kingsley gave them a generous hearing and his loyal friendship. He, for one, was not afraid that the whole structure of spiritual values would come tumbling down around the heads of men for their being honestly inquisitive. And to prove it he wrote a glorious fairy-tale, *The Water Babies*. Special Creation, indeed—the fairy who had learned to make real, living butterflies came to Mother Carey to boast. "But Mother Carey laughed. Know, silly child, that anyone can make things, if they take time and trouble enough: but it is not everyone who, like me, can make things make themselves."

DARWIN AND MODERN SCIENCE

IF WE are true believers and accept those basic tenets of science—the conservation of matter and energy—we are ready to accept the artist's tradition of influence. After all, the eye can trace the unbroken series of expanding ripples when a stone is tossed into a quiet pond. The world is never the same after any event, however trivial.

"Thou canst not pluck a flower
without troubling some bright star."

Unfortunately for those who would trace the influence of any creative mind or character, the world of human thought and action is no quiet pond. It is instead a deep and surging sea with countless forces at work below its surface and upon its unresting face. On such turbulent waters even the boiling wake of a huge vessel soon merges into the general activity. To follow out the course of influence with honest certainty is precarious business. And the natural scientist is likely to feel considerable reserve toward the efforts of his colleagues in the humane arts and letters when they set themselves to tracing "influences."

Thus it is a delicate, as well as a difficult matter to attempt to trace the influence of Darwin upon our modern world in this year of Grace nearly seventy years beyond the time of his passing. There can be no question that such influence is powerful and continuing, as is that of Newton. Yet to identify and isolate it with anything like complete fairness and certainty in a task bordering on the impossible.

We must repeat that the idea of evolution was not original with Darwin. At least two men before his time had sketched the outlines of natural selection. Wallace had thought it out independently while Darwin was at work. The name of Malthus is not indexed in the *Origin of Species,* yet we know from Darwin's statements elsewhere how deeply he, like Wallace, was indebted to the *Essay on Population.* Modern genetics was foreseen by Darwin and was, in a sense, an outgrowth of his work on variation. Yet its methods and its principles stem from his contemporary Mendel, whose work lay neglected for more than a generation. We are in difficulty when we talk of Darwin's influence on the modern world.

Perhaps the honest and hopeful approach is to assume that genius is a matter of process, giving form and expression to whatever, old or new, it works upon. And if we can show that the kind of process which so nobly characterized the work and spirit of Darwin has become integral to our modern civilization, we may rest our case as to his influence. The immediate question then becomes, what was the essential genius of Darwin?

First and foremost Darwin advanced, by example, the right of free inquiry and discussion, so long as it goes hand in hand with a scrupulous examination of the evidence. Second, he advanced the concept of process, not the being, but the becoming. Far and above everything else that Darwin means, these two principles stand forth clear and uncompromising. And because he was working, not on problems of inanimate nature, but on the problem of life itself, his activities have touched the very nerve center of static authority. Since 1859 there has never been any question as to the fundamental issues.

It is of course vastly important that Darwin was the first to make reasonable and convincing a very old idea—that of organic evolution with its emphasis on the kinship and continuity of nature. Others had talked of it, a few had toiled over it. Characteristically, Darwin went hunting for it. The work of his powerful imagination and persistent energy suggests the superbly trained bird dogs which he loved, deliberately and thoroughly exploring the field, step by step, nostrils alert, never breaking, never flinching, never diverted until the last fluttering single had been accounted for.

It is of lesser importance whether Darwin established evolution as a fact—whether he proved it in reality to have occurred. Actually he did not, although his work made the idea finally reasonable. Evolution became at length respectable as a theory and a point of view from which science might proceed to further inquiry.

Least important to us—and this must seem a strange way in which to deal with a mighty concept—is Darwin's particular explanation of the mechanism of evolution. The origin of species by natural selection is most generally and intimately associated with his name, and he would be aggrieved to have it otherwise, we may be certain. This idea is, however, less the essence of the man than an expression of that essence. Though conceivably the theory might collapse, its author would still stand solid and immense, an imposing figure in the human adventure. But we shall probably not have to deal with such a collapse. The operation of natural selection has been demonstrated by critical experiments in the field of genetics to be a potent factor in the organic world.

The immediate effect of Darwin upon science was one of magnificent release. It was not, properly speaking, a stimulus—the vast unexplored world of the unknown was stimulus enough and curiosity was straining to understand it. Darwin cut the leash and the human mind leaped ahead.

See what he did for classification. The first task of science is to catalog and describe. Think in how many ways one might classify the houses in a small town—as to location, cost, date, color, material, size, number of occupants, form, and so on. Precisely this sort of problem had long engaged the minds of naturalists confronted, as we know now, by more than a million kinds of living plants and animals. At first the chief concern of naturalists had been merely to tell the kinds apart and give to each some designation. But by the 19th century, with every continent opened by exploration, revealing countless strange forms of life, a far more effective system of classification was imperative.

To go back for a moment to the houses in a village, the banker, the artist, historian, or police officer would each have his own *basis* on which to classify them. Without a conscious basis, classification is naive, almost futile. Francis Bacon, who had insisted that nature be asked fair questions, was equally insistent that the scientist be aware of his own mental processes. The naturalists of the 18th and early 19th centuries had vastly improved the techniques for classifying plants and animals. But until the doctrine of evolution emerged as more than a shadowy guess, the basic theory and purpose of their efforts were almost as primitive as the motives of the tribal medicine man collecting herbs. It is enough for him to tell the kinds apart and have names for them.

Organic evolution proclaimed that all life was a continuum in time and all living organisms related by common descent. This meant that organisms could, and must, be grouped by appropriate resemblances and differences so as to reflect their degrees of relationship. Here was a system to end all other systems. Plant and animal geography now opened up new vistas. The geological history of continents and islands became an integral part of classification, for the presence of related groups in areas now isolated from each other had to be accounted for.

It is an error to suppose as many do that classification is an outmoded phase of natural history. It affords a continuing test of evolutionary doctrine. The increasing refinement of biological study requires greater certainty than ever before of the identity of animals and plants used in experimental work. The fact that all organisms are now considered to be part of one great family tree is a challenge to the intelligence and skill of the classifier who must reconstruct that tree. Actually the business of classification has today greater vitality and significance than ever before, thanks to Darwin.

The effect of the Darwinian release upon the study of

form and structure has been no less remarkable. Cuvier, Owen, and Agassiz, master anatomists all, had bitterly opposed the idea of organic evolution. Yet their comparisons of the structures of animals in different groups had shown the existence of basic patterns—for example, in the extremities. The wing of bird and bat, the human arm, and the flipper of the seal, all represent variations of a common skeletal theme. As early as 1851 the botanist Hofmeister, in a work of superlative genius, had shown the existence of a fundamental plan in the life histories of various plant groups. To the Special Creationist such findings could never be more than a curious footnote on theology, and something of a reflection upon the inventiveness of an omnipotent Creator, apparently obliged, as are most of the rest of us, to worry about cutting and fitting, with a limited repertoire of ideas.

But what a transfiguration such facts undergo if viewed by the evolutionist! The homologies of form and life history at once become the most reasonable, most natural kind of phenomena, attesting the slow course of modification and adjustment through the ages. The stone which the anatomists had quarried became the corner of the edifice which they thought could not be built. And new generations of comparative anatomists have not only strengthened the evidence for evolution, but have found in it the source of their most fruitful and significant efforts. In fact the anatomical case for evolution is so pat and so conveniently presented that other and equally important aspects of biology are often slighted in the teaching of that subject.

Studies of the problems of behavior in plants and animals, of their diseases, and of their past history have profited incalculably from the fresh viewpoint which evolution affords. In all of these fields it makes a tremendous practical difference whether one starts by regarding each species as a special creation and thus, in great measure, a law unto itself, or whether one assumes that a common thread of relationship runs through the whole organic world.

Some years ago a doctoral thesis on a proper diet for white mice was made to sound absurd by the newspapers. It is absurd if one sees no possible correlation between mice and men. But precisely such a thesis has helped safeguard the health, and even save the lives, of countless human infants through showing the need of all animal bodies for vitamins, etc. No one questions that geological studies have been fruitful in finding the metals and fossil fuels that keep our modern industrial life going. But this work of the geologist is built squarely upon the notion that fossils register the passing of time by their position in the evolutionary scale. A geologist who does not believe that the reptiles are more ancient than the birds, and that ferns are of greater antiquity than palmtrees, belongs with doctors who let blood for every disease. His practical work would be equally futile.

Psychology, that very special aspect of behavior which was for so long a province of philosophy and introspection, has expanded its scope under the influence of evolutionary doctrine and become an experimental science. It has made eager and profitable use of all that can be learned from a comparative study of the nervous systems of animals at every level. The intricate and baffling processes of the human mind have become more understandable as we have assumed them to be the product of a long prehuman past. They have certainly been illuminated by our growing knowledge of neuromuscular behavior in many groups of the animal kingdom.

It seems fair to say that the sciences which deal with inanimate nature have also been influenced by the Darwinian release, although the question is difficult. Newton had given these sciences a dynamic concept of the universe, true. Yet its operation had the character of being fixed into a pattern that seemed practically static. Darwin opened up the possibility that the universe itself might be the expression of an infinitely long process. And presently cosmic science became, not static nor simply dynamic in its outlook, but truly genetic. Worlds, even solar systems and galaxies of them, are now considered to be the expressions of change and development.

So far as the planet Earth was concerned, geologists had even before Darwin laid a foundation for the concept of process, by their assumption of the uniform action, throughout the history of the earth, of existing natural laws. This led them back to the problem of the origin of our own planet, and by logical steps, to that of the evolution of our solar system. Meanwhile the astronomers were piling up and analyzing their meticulous observations of the visible universe, finding that even the eternal stars bear witness to the unceasing process of genetic change. And the spectroscope was revealing that the most remote of visible bodies are composed of the familiar chemical elements of our periodic table.

This table is sometimes referred to as a sort of genealogical or evolutionary tree of the chemical elements. It does give the basis for dealing with an ancient intuition—the transmutation of elements, for in it they are arranged in an orderly series, *as though* they were genetically derived from simple beginnings. It is fair to say that the most refined discoveries of atomic science and the mathematical analyses of theoretical physics both emphasize the significance of process. And so far as philosophical relativity is concerned, the cast of evolutionary thought has served to bridge the gap between it and the classical Newtonian concept of a universe fixed and ordained.

For a long time the exact physical sciences have thrown a spell over the students of life. Biological inquiries have generally been fruitful in proportion to the energy spent on the quest for physical explanations, reducible to mathematical terms, for in the spectrum of the sciences mathematics is at one extreme of precision, biology at the other. And so it is that biologists have felt that certainty lay in the physical analysis of biological phenomena. The secrets of the living universe must be hid in mechanistic control and determinism!

Yet the deeper that physical scientists (as distinct from students of living organisms) have probed in their search for the ultimate, the greater has become their modesty and uncertainty. True, they have vastly extended the certainties of human operation. But while matter and energy can be manipulated more effectively than ever before, their meaning, and the meaning of the universe which they compose, seem to recede as analysis advances. Truth at this extreme of natural knowledge becomes a matter of statistical probabilities, and the very forms into which it can be cast are relative, in no sense absolute. The firm finality which the biologist had hoped to find when his physical and mathematical analysis of life was completed proves to be a dancing, spinning, elusive cloud of particles.

And because of this, the world of knowledge has witnessed a strange spectacle. While the biologist—at least the strictly mechanistic biologist—has been stumbling along in the wake of physical science in its gropings after the ultimate nature of matter and energy, his brother the physicist has doubled back in his search for meaning and certainty. He has learned that these qualities are to be sought, not in ultimate components, but in the organization of these components into higher systems. Returning a compliment with vigor, he is back in the very dooryard of the biologist. The men who have been personally in the thick of atomic studies, who have trudged to the very North Pole of material science, have suddenly become the keepers of social conscience. They have begun to concern themselves with human ethics—rightly fearful that knowledge, without morality, may bring destruction to mankind.

Now if we accept the evolutionary point of view, it is fair to say that enlightened ethical behavior and the religious forms which are its essence represent the highest present reaches of evolution. On the same basis, atomic behavior represents the raw material of evolution, so far as it has been discoverable to this time. To use a well-worn example, one can make a serviceable timepiece from a variety of materials. Its meaning for us depends less upon its composition than upon the way it has been put together, and the resultant operation in accord, of course, with physical principles.

Small wonder then that the physical scientists have turned about (not in their investigations, but in their concern). Matter and energy can only have meaning for us in terms of form and the process by which form has been attained. One of the greatest of these scientists, in a noble protest against the misuse of knowledge for destruction, insists that the function of science is to ease the burdens of mankind. Actually there is a higher function—to interpret man and the universe to man, and to make clear his responsible relation to that universe. Analysis of the raw material of evolution, alone, will never do this. We must consider its highest reaches, and the process by which they have been attained. So it is that the physicist, recoiling in horror, is appealing to the conscience of mankind.

But before we proceed with this intriguing problem, there are more prosaic matters to be discussed. Darwin's work had carried in it the seed of two new aspects of natural science. One of them—the science of variation and inheritance, now called genetics—he had clearly predicted. The other was implicit in his thesis, and to it in 1866 Haeckel gave the name *Oecology*. Darwin had really made it impossible, except as an arbitrary and provisional device, to think of life apart from environment. Biochemistry had already, in its earliest phases, shown life to be dependent upon a continuing interchange of material and energy with the environment. But Darwin went even farther, asserting as he did that environment had from the beginning built itself into the very form and organization of all forms of life. And so Darwin, dealing primarily with the interrelations of life and environment, was thus himself one of the first and greatest of ecologists. Yet by some curious perversity he is mentioned only casually, if at all, in most treatises on ecology.

Darwin had said, "A grand and almost untrodden field of inquiry will be opened, on the causes and laws of variation, on correlation, on the effects of use and disuse, on the direct action of external conditions, and so forth." He actually labored to open up this field. In a sense he was perhaps handicapped by the grandeur which he saw in it, as he certainly was by prevailing notions among breeders. Too often it was the practice to search for explanation by working back from the individual product of heredity to its ancestors. Since the number of ancestors must double with each generation, the limitations of this method are severe.

Meanwhile, his unknown contemporary, the Abbot Gregor Mendel, was beginning very simply with known ancestors and keeping account of their progeny through the ensuing generations. He was clean-cut in his methods and happy in his choice of material—the garden pea. With classical simplicity he formulated the basic principles of modern genetics, announcing that the determining units of heredity are assorted, transmitted, and recombined according to statistical principles without being altered in the process. The operation can be compared somewhat to the shuffling, dealing, and making up of hands in bridge, each card preserving its identity through successive hands while the values of the hands depend upon the combinations which make them up. Because Mendel was not of the scientific elect, he was obliged to look to the German botanist Nägeli for endorsement. Nägeli turned down his tyrant's thumb and that was the end of the matter until 1900.

The 20th century has seen genetics grow mightily. The carriers of hereditary units have been identified within the visible chromosomes of the living cell and are called genes. Natural selection has been shown in actual operation, eliminating unfavorable variations due to new combinations of genes, or modification of old ones. The genes themselves have been modified experimentally by external conditions. There is no evidence as yet, however, that environment can be counted upon to produce particularly favorable qualities, or that use and disuse have any effect on the genes. Darwin gave some thought to both possibilities. To date it seems as though he was at his wise best in simply assuming that variations occur and then survive or perish according to their fitness.

Persistently, however, the students of fossil plants and animals, and many of the classifiers of living ones, have contended that Darwinism overlooks a potent factor, an innate tendency in living things to evolve in a definite, almost predetermined, direction through the ages. This they call orthogenesis. A classical instance is that of the horse, whose orderly progress from a five-toed to a one-toed animal is remarkably documented by fossil skeletons. It is as though the horse "knew all the time" in which direction it was evolving.

Among the flowering plants the believers in orthogenesis point out that there are several lines of descent which, after they branched apart long ago, have moved ahead in almost parallel directions. These ideas are welcomed by many philosophers, who speak of inner guiding principles in life, or vital urge, and the like. But experimental scientists view such suggestions coldly, and naturally can do little to prove or disprove them in the short span of time covered by controlled experiments. On the whole the evidence to date gathered in the laboratory suggests that inheritable variations are unpredictable, thus justifying Darwin.

Certainly the great continental grasslands in which the horse evolved are very ancient and seem to have offered a very steady sort of environment while the horse was slowly changing to fit that environment with ever greater perfection. The selectionists have a point there. And the flowering plants have evolved step by step with the orders of insects in a binding, reciprocal relationship which has limited and doubtless selected the successful variations in both. It looks as though the advocates of orthogenesis must be long content with nothing better than a Scotch verdict.

In the field of biochemistry it has been shown that each species of organism has its own characteristic type of proteins, and calculation shows that a practically unlimited number of distinct proteins may exist. But their separation by conventional chemical methods is often not possible, so delicate and complicated are the differences. More than this, the influence of chemical messengers—the hormones—upon development and behavior is now well established, and their study has become one of the most delicate enterprises of science. That they are vitally concerned in the process of evolution can no longer be doubted.

Much that Darwin thought has been substantiated. Much that is new has been learned, both about the way in which evolution has taken place and the results of it. A vast amount remains to be learned, and the search will be fruitful in proportion to our respect for his method of open-minded inquiry and scrupulous weighing of evidence.

We have seen the influence, both of his ideas and his example on fields of knowledge which were in existence during his day and on those which have been opened up since, in no small measure as a consequence of his work.

His genius is an enduring part of our present civilization.

A NEW MIRROR

EVOLUTION, like the disgusted drill-sergeant, orders Man to step out in front and look at himself. Most of us can be reasonable and serene enough until the turn of conversation, or events, hits home. When it does, the real test begins. Human self-esteem was not flattered by the suggestion of our sub-human ancestry.

Actually the *Origin of Species* had very little to say about man the human species, *Homo sapiens*. But the inference was clear from the first, and by 1871 Darwin was ready to express himself on the central problem—*The Descent or Origin of Man*—"the main conclusion" of which "is that man is descended from some less highly organized form." The book is a *tour de force*—a prodigious feat of scientific erudition, marshalling every obtainable bit of evidence that might bear on the problem, and presenting a brief that has not been seriously threatened since. More reliance is placed upon use and disuse and upon sexual selection as factors in man's evolution than a cautious modern biologist would like. But the main argument, based on development, structures, behavior, and geographical facts, still stands, argument in the meantime being reenforced by very respectable fossil evidence of early man.

Darwin, characteristically, is more concerned that his evidence be accurate than with any pride in his views. "False facts are highly injurious . . . false views, if supported by some evidence, do little harm, for everyone takes a salutary pleasure in proving their falseness." Having tossed this bone to his scientific and philosophical critics, he has others in reserve for those who might object on religious grounds. He affirms that we are all descended from barbarians and proceeds to contrast some of the savages he had known with animals whose magnanimous behavior was a matter of record. But elsewhere, and more important, he makes clear his refusal to see in man's history the operation of blind chance, and in the origin of man anything more miraculous than the birth of the individual. "The understanding revolts" at seeing anything but the operation of universal law in a "grand sequence of events." Religious writing records few more profound statements of essential faith.

Many of the findings of science which can be traced to the evolutionary viewpoint might eventually have been swallowed without too much protest. But the clear implication with regard to Man's origin stuck in many throats. The western world had not been conditioned for such a strong dose. Its political, economic, and religious leaders had employed all manner of devices in the exercise of their functions, and flattery was not the least of these. Napoleon had told his armies that every French soldier carries a marshal's baton in his knapsack. The humblest British workman, with proof before his eyes, could see that an exemplary practice of diligence would enable him to stand before kings. Priests, preachers, and the holy writings which they expounded made capital by contrasting the spiritual with the bestial. Any suggestion of the animal nature or background of humanity was not agreeable—it was not even tolerable. It was to be suppressed, despised, and kept in the dark cellar if it could not be destroyed.

The probability that man might be akin to the ape was perhaps less completely a surprise than most people pretended. The kinship of all races of mankind, regardless of color or culture was a solid part of the Hebrew-Christian tradition, although the traditional basis of racial separation was neither scientific nor edifying. So far as the human body is concerned, if we except the usually misunderstood saying that Man is made in the image of God, the new view of man's animal origin was all gain and no loss.

The human body had been badly treated and at times worse regarded in many societies which were beyond the stage of savagery. And while the theological concepts of Incarnation and Resurrection invested it with the dignity of a Temple, it was too often, even in Christian lands the object of unspeakable neglect and hardship, if not revolting cruelty. Nor were matters always improved by changing concepts of the nature, origin, and meaning of sin. Flesh and Devil!

The flea-ridden filth of the Middle Ages, the anaemic features shown in medieval art, the small size of the fabulous knights whose armor is still preserved, the records of famine and plague, and the abominable health conditions of the industrial revolution, all stand in accusing contrast to the care and skill lavished upon draft and riding horses, hunting dogs, dairy cattle, and the sheep whose wool was a mainstay of mercantile Europe. It took the crippled Michelangelo to do as the Greeks had done and once more identify physical vigor and beauty with divinity, while Dürer, da Vinci, Rubens, and the whole group of artists nurtured in the cleanly, hearty Lowlands at least went so far as to see beauty in vigor and health. Rabelais briefed the case for vitality in his own way, too. But knowledge and practice lagged far behind, as they usually do. Young George Washington walked into the smallpox for the sake of protocol, and wore the scars for his lifetime. The code demanded that he and his brother make an official call at a Governor's palace which today would be in quarantine.

With evolution, the clear assertion of the animal origin and character of the human body supplied an intellectual basis for a new interest in physical health. More than that, it supplied powerful means for doing something about the problem, sanctioning the most complete and exhaustive study of the body as a physical and biological system. Unsanitary conditions, malnutrition, and disease are not the objectives of medical art—they are its obstacles. The objective is health. In any great campaign the end sought must be clearly understood before obstacles can be dealt with effectively.

It is impossible to know how much credit should go to Darwinism for the amazing progress in care of the human body that has come about since 1859. Trained physicians—witness Asa Gray and Agassiz—were divided on the question of evolution. Louis Pasteur, whose contribution to medicine was immeasurable, was an opponent of the doctrine. Yet there can be no doubt that research and practice in the fields of microbiology, nutrition, and human physiology, have been carried on in an atmosphere of conscious evolutionary belief.

The animal character of the human body has been accepted as an axiom during the period of most brilliant and substantial medical progress. The validity of animal experimentation rests upon this axiom and the results have more than justified the assumption. The horse pours diphtheria antitoxin from his bloodstream into ours, while a far more distant cousin, the common frog, reacts in most interesting and useful fashion when supplied with the urine of a pregnant woman.

Primitive Christianity had not been much kinder to the human mind than to the body. True, Paul saw in the products of Greek thought something formidable to be dealt with. From time to time the Church made such concessions to the intellect as lay within its discretion and power—some of them handsome. Body and mind, however, were considered to be separate entities, subservient to a third, the soul. The soul, by its very nature, was beyond the reach of scientific methods of investigation, yet its prerogative was supreme, demanding conformity to its best interests both from bodily activities and thought. Since both of these last are deeply influenced by habit, training and habit logically become matters of the greatest importance. A great deal of empirical knowledge concerning both was accumulated before the 18th century, and an extremely efficient system of teaching developed by the Jesuits on the basis of such knowledge. In this respect they were preeminent.

Meanwhile physical science, or natural philosophy as it was then called, was beginning to discover and organize the kind of knowledge necessary to a rational explanation of the senses. Also during the 18th century the claims of both body and mind to dignified consideration were being urged by rationalist and romanticist in varying degree. A growing number of men, among them Erasmus Darwin, were beginning to insist that there must be a physical or bodily basis for human thought. Physicians familiar with the stages of delirium were not hard to convince. Such a functional view of thought was exactly what was needed to get on with any science of the mind. No phase of experience had been more cumbered with preconceptions. As Höffding shrewdly pointed out, psychology is "no more bound to begin with an explanation of what the soul is than physics is bound to begin with an explanation of what matter is."

By the time Charles Darwin published the *Origin of Species,* a modern, experimental, and inductive study of the mind had been launched and was under way. Thus Darwin's influence was that of a favoring wind—a powerful reenforcement. He personally gave his attention to the troublesome problem of instinct, and later that of the emotions. If his psychology seems quaint by modern standards, his zeal in collecting data and his honesty in trying to interpret them have had a lasting influence.

Present-day psychology is frankly evolutionary in its viewpoint, and is justified by its fruits. But let it never be forgotten that the psychologist has a peculiarly hard assignment. The mind is at once the object of his study and the instrument through which he passes judgment on this object. Mental phenomena are so complex, so intimately significant, and so elusive that numerous "schools" of psychology have inevitably been established. Any biologist knows how difficult it is, when working near the limits of power of the microscope, to avoid seeing what one wants to see. The psychologist faces the same problem when he gets near the fringe of his available evidence. Only with the greatest difficulty can he avoid making the wish be father to the thought.

Psychologists are about as far from agreement as the rest of us on such ancient problems as freedom of the will. But it is safe to say that their studies of conditioned behavior and the learning process in vertebrate animals have shown that important elements in the psychology of man were in existence long before man appeared on earth. Darwin had stated that the mental powers of the higher animals are the same in kind as those of man, but different in degree. This statement is not wholly clear, or if clear, not wholly proved. Even if true there is no question that the gap between man and any other animal is profound and that the human race is a distinct and unique biological entity. At least we know now that men of all races and colors are human beings! Here as elsewhere, applied Darwinism has done far more to elevate than to degrade.

The scientist in any field of inquiry must and can only do the best he can. This is a point often misunderstood by the non-scientist. We have always allowed the mathematician his initial assumptions. Men in political, religious, artistic, and economic work usually make their own without so much as by-your-leave. Those whose object of inquiry is the human mind must often, in order to get on with their work, deliberately make assumptions which will simplify matters for the time being. This is true of the behaviorists in psychology, who have drawn so much lightning about their heads. They have said, "Let us assume as we proceed that the human mind is an expression of physical processes in the nervous system, a product of the slow evolution of that nervous system, and a manifestation of stimulus and response. On this basis, what can we discover?" Such a procedure is entirely legitimate, and does not deny the right of anyone else to go to work on any other set of assumptions he may please to make. Yet anguished howls of indignation have greeted the behaviorists. When do they come and why?

We can understand those philosophers who object on principle to any verdict of the human mind which tends to reflect upon the validity of human judgment and the general importance of the mind. We must also allow for a certain measure of irrepressible mischief on the part of the behaviorists themselves. But mostly, I surmise, we must reckon with those undisciplined camp followers who imagine that they understand grand strategy at their remote distance from the high command.

Visualize a professor of limited capacity, but equipped with a neatly trimmed van Dyke, a speech as neatly clipped, an impressive repertoire of technical terms, and a ready way with the microscope. He tells his adoring group of premedical students what is perfectly true—that the oxygen consumption of the central nervous system keeps pace with its activity; then solemnly asks, "Do you see, gentlemen, what this means?" Allowing for a suitably dramatic pause, he relieves their suspense. "It means, gentlemen, that human thought is nothing but a form of oxidation." And his disciples, good honest apprentices that they are, untrained in logic and the subtleties of dialectic, untrained even in judging the validity of evidence, swallow it whole. The story gets around, the humanists fume, and the religious explode.

Of course we touch on delicate and difficult matters when we deal with, and particularly when we attempt to use, the science of the mind. Where does applied psychology cross the vague boundary between bettered human relations and callous exploitation in such matters as "human engineering" (a barbarous term) or "salesmanship"? Great is the power of suggestion, and heavy the moral burden upon those endowed with it—thrice heavy if they are able to reenforce an intuitive skill with techniques drawn from science.

There is no nobler challenge than the relief of mental illness. Yet the darkness of this realm of grim shadows at times almost envelops the healers who would snatch back its victims into the light of day. Unjust and flippant the epigram which says of one school of psychiatry, "It *is* the disease which it pretends to cure." Yet what kernel of truth may there be in this saying?

Because the mind is an expression of physical process the welfare of the body is basic to the healing of the mind. Disorders of the central nervous system must be remedied or adjusted so far as possible. The machinery which sustains mind must be in order. But that is not all. This mechanism operates within the human body as its immediate environment. That immediate environment, so profoundly sensitive to the balance of its own internal secretions, must likewise be in order. Medical knowledge is fundamental in the treatment of mental illness. But if psychiatry is based upon medical knowledge, it does not stop there. It has to deal with patterns of thought and emotion which have failed, in some way, to meet the requirements of normal living. By the very nature of the problem, those who deal with it must face the fact that the individual patient is inseparably part of a larger whole, the culture in which he lives. One does not have to accept all of the doctrines of Sigmund Freud, or of any other particular leader in the field of psychiatry to grant that a transformation has begun in our efforts to understand and deal with the question of mental health.

Those efforts now rest squarely upon the assumption that the human personality is itself an expression of process. The evolutionary past is written into our make-up. What we become is a resultant of that past, interacting with our present world of experience. If our bodies are healthy, our inheritance from the past is normal and the interaction between individual and environment is harmonious and consistent, we are well integrated and have mental health.

Man the animal must somehow, without damage to his integrity, be also man the civilized and spiritual being. For example, the strains which are now and then put upon personality (not to mention law and order) by our insistence upon a universal standard of monogamy are obvious. But we need to remember that, in a society which sanctions plural marriage as a practical obligation, the individual who inclines toward monogamy has been observed to develop feelings of inferiority and maladjustment, ending in neurotic disturbances as definite as the clinical symptoms so often observed in our own culture. Such an individual may feel as guilty as Samuel Pepys after one of his amorous forays.

Since such reflections bring up the problems of good and evil, of sin and guilt, I venture that much might be gained from a theological glossary, written so far as possible in language acceptable to the scientist. Initiative, of course, would have to come from the theologians, since they are in less agreement among themselves than the scientists. Even so, they agree on much, and it should never be forgotten that their work is, viewed as coldly as possible, an effort to meet a tremendous practical problem of mankind.

Crime is an offense against society; vice, against one's self. Sin is an offense against the laws of God. The idea of guilt is associated with all. In a technical sense, both Christ and Socrates were condemned as criminals. In the eyes of their societies they were sinners, too—a judgment which the evolving conscience of mankind has gloriously reversed.

Science has at least given man new and deeper conceptions of the consequences of his actions. So far as it has attended the problem, it has also shown that while conscience is a badge of our humanity, an unwarranted feeling of guilt is poor stuff for the fabric of a personality or a community. The theologian, in a world of increasing literacy and scientific knowledge, should welcome these contributions, and for his part, be more cautious than ever in interpreting the Will of God. The needless multiplication of sins may be as bad for theology as the needless multiplication of causes is bad for science.

The studies of human cultures begun in Darwin's time by Lubbock, later Lord Avebury, and the analysis of human sexual behavior by a younger contemporary, Havelock Ellis, have placed in the record a whole body of evidence to show how complicated are the forces which take part in the shaping of personality and adjusting it to the business of living. New generations of anthropologists, biologists, and social psychologists have pressed forward with their studies, piling up and refining the evidence until it can no longer be denied. And the abundant testimony of psychiatrists has revealed how extensive and corroding is the mischief wrought when we attempt to ignore and override man's physical nature, denying its proper place in the whole scheme of being, and treating it as something apart.

The problem of personality is thus taking on new and agonizing dimensions. It is painful business, when one has been lying in a cramped position for a long time, to stretch out, stand erect, and try to assume full stature. Man is finding that there is much more to himself than he had been led to believe, and it hurts.

Dazed and stumbling, he is bound to make errors. But this does not mean, as many would have us believe, that he is demoralized. He is feeling his way toward a new and more comprehensive ethics which will enjoin the achievement of health rather than the avoidance of disease. There is a difference, as any physician of body or mind can testify.

So much emphasis had been placed on struggle, competition, and conflict by the advocates of Darwinism that an even more important point, that of harmony, growth, and wholeness, had been neglected. Darwin saw this problem clearly, particularly in his *Descent of Man,* where he emphasized the beneficent role of such constructive forces as mutual aid and ethical behavior. Huxley, the scarred but buoyant veteran of evolutionary controversy, did not give these constructive principles the attention they deserved, and his final views, expressed shortly before his death, are somewhat depressing. Since it was his wit and artistry which largely interpreted Darwinism to the popular mind, the limitations of his emphasis have been unfortunate. To these problems we shall return in a later chapter.

The essence of Darwinism is its integrative character. It was in no sense an analytical attempt to take the clock apart, pile its parts in a heap, and then pretend that their simple sum, the heap, was as good as a clock. Instead of assuming that man was something aloof and apart from nature, and that living organisms were divorced somehow from their physical surroundings, Darwinism saw the natural universe as a magnificent organic system, a process whose components, each a system in itself, were in principle and in fact, inseparable from the total unity. Following this conception one step further, and seeing in this dynamic unity the expression of energy, we arrive at a conception not merely of system, but of process, the interplay of forces and materials.

Here at length was a clue to the riddle of human behavior. Physical science was already at work on the laws which govern process in the non-living world. Psychology, using the tools of physics and anatomy, was well under way with its analytic study of sensation and response. What was needed was an integrating principle. Philosophers had long been familiar with the idea of process and the problem of integration. But they were not wholly accustomed to the humdrum discipline of inductive fact. The materials were ready, and the time was ripe for something to happen.

Into this supersaturated solution the seed-crystal of maturing Darwinism was dropped and the whole began to take discernible shape. Gestalt psychology and its variants were soon outlined. Human behavior in fact revealed itself as a dynamic pattern of lesser patterns, all functionally related, all the expression of development with respect to each other and the environment. From such a working, and workable concept, came order, provisional order perhaps, but tangible and useful, something which the science of man could use as a basis for getting on with its task. And the sequel has been immensely fruitful.

By the beginning of the 20th century the science of mind and personality was being rewritten on a frankly evolutionary basis and some philosophers were conceding that their business was not with the act of thinking, but with the products of that activity. A stubborn problem, however, persisted, and for it Darwin himself was in some measure responsible. He had laid great emphasis on the slow accumulation of minute variations as the mode of evolution. He pictured the process as a continuous curve, with no breaks or jumps, each new phenomenon growing imperceptibly out of the preceding and thus obviously related to it. Man had come to differ from the ape, and by infinite extension backward in time, from the amoeba, "in degree rather than in kind."

But common sense is entitled to its day in science as elsewhere. And common sense simply has to deal with certain quite definite qualities, distinctive orders of phenomena, which can be observed in man but not in the ape, and with many qualities in both which have not been detected in the lowest forms of life.

The data of biological science reenforced the claims of common sense at this point. William Bateson in 1894 had shown that variations found in nature are not continuous in any familiar sense. Instead of forming an unbroken chain of almost imperceptible differences, moving step by step through related forms, they resemble jumps, or breaks, between species whose common origin is evident enough. The Dutchman de Vries, some years later, put forth his mutation theory, and although his interpretation was not verified, no one questions today the appearance, from time to time, of such mutations, sports, or jumps. There can be new things under the sun.

Actually the problem of novelty, of new qualities, was not itself new. The skeptical French had their saying, "Plus ça change, plus c'est la même chose." The Special Creationists could shrug it off as God's business, not theirs. But the pedestrian evolutionists, bound to their dogged search for continuity and efficient causes, had to face the issue. Lloyd Morgan, a philosopher, psychologist, and one time student of Huxley's, finally came forward with a reasonable suggestion, which he called Emergent Evolution. Actually the idea, which is simple and commends itself to common sense, was familiar to philosophers. Morgan took care to state it so that it would do no violence to scientific fact.

When two gases, hydrogen and oxygen, are merely mixed, the mixture has the properties of a gas, predictable by what we know about each constituent. But a spark will cause the two to combine chemically in definite proportions. When this happens, a new kind of substance, the liquid water, appears. Water has properties of its own, not predictable on the basis of anything we know about the two gases which go into its composition. A new set of qualities has appeared by virtue of a new relationship among old things. This represents a distinct break, a jump and not an imperceptible transition. It is an emergent phenomenon. We know by our experiment and can demonstrate by later analysis that water contains two parts of hydrogen by volume to one of oxygen. But only experience with water itself will tell us the properties of this new system made up of old components.

Beginning with a simple inorganic illustration such as this, Morgan and those who follow him have extended the idea to higher and more complex phenomena, into the organic world, and on through the series of organisms to man. Life is treated as an emergent and, at higher levels, so are human personality, even divinity. As the operation of a watch emerges from the way in which its parts are formed and put together, so with the thing we call life. Which, by and large, seems like a sensible and useful way to consider the problem and so to get ahead with our study of it.

Darwin's obsession with continuity was justified, for process (and life is a process) is continuous. Everything that exists is the expression of a sequence that is unbroken, and orderly. There are no real interruptions in this ceaseless activity. But what does happen is that, from time to time, new orders of reality make their appearance—water from two gases, a sphere from a group of sister cells, poetry from words—or harmony. "That out of three sounds . . . frame, not a fourth sound, but a star." Science can go on contentedly about its business of collecting *data*—i.e., those things which are given it to know—accepting their diversity and reading back into their fundamental unity.

On these terms the idealist can get his foot through the door which Darwin opened, with every assurance that he cannot wreck the edifice that science is building, nor scientists destroy our system of values and idealism.

A SOCIAL BEING

"EVERYONE," says Darwin in his *Descent of Man,* "will admit that man is a social being." And with characteristic thoroughness, he explores some of the implications of that statement. His humanity and even his insight are likely to surprise the average reader, who has been accustomed to hear that Darwin's ideas were eagerly seized upon by those who wished to justify a ruthless individualism.

Now your true buccaneer is seldom a philosopher, and still less often a man of conscience in search of justification. He insists on his own right to be ruthless, but wants others to be meek. The suggestion that they have a right to fight back does not serve his purpose. He prefers to have his victims fed on a pale diet of non-resistance, rather than on the red meat of competition. Actually the conservative social philosophies probably have less to say of any debt to Darwinism than does the modern gospel of extreme socialization.

But while the practitioners of unrestricted private enterprise were busy practicing it, there arose a group of followers to out-Darwin Darwin—the neo-Darwinians. To them competition had the force of a universal scientific and moral law. They thought mainly in terms of competition between individuals, and paid little heed to the fact that organisms must somehow adjust themselves to the collaborative life of the group. Nature was red in tooth and claw, life was a soulless, materialistic enterprise, and the individual had either to eat or be eaten. It was through the eyes of these uninvited evangels that Darwin was seen by many in the world at large, and no one can be blamed much for not liking the picture. Interpreted by such philosophers as the German Nietzsche, it was to have tragic consequences for mankind.

Actually Darwin had pointed out that mutual aid, compassion, and the higher human virtues were indispensable to the survival of mankind. He did not ignore the struggle between social groups—who could, unless he were blind to the course of history? But he showed that the trend was toward the coalescence of such groups, and thus toward the expansion of the principle of collaboration. But the neo-Darwinians, who had gone all out on the matter of struggle and competition, extending it to the very cells and organs of the individual body, paid little heed to these observations of the master.

It remained for a man not trained as a biologist, the philosopher Prince Kropotkin, to meet the neo-Darwinians with something other than religious wrath. He attempted, in fact, to meet them on their own ground by gathering scientific evidence to show that the principle of mutual aid within the species was a widespread biological phenomenon. If this could be demonstrated, it would show that the higher social virtues of man were not operating against the inertia of a universal moral law, but were built upon and reenforced by a prolonged evolutionary history. They would thus be a part of the organic fiber of man, not something working against the grain.

Kropotkin was vulnerable, mainly because he was outside the professional brotherhood of zoologists, but also because he did not use controlled experiment. He had to collect from whatever sources he could, as Darwin did. What was allowed to the master was intolerable in a disciple who disagreed with the majority. But at least Kropotkin registered a protest and opened the way for an eventual consideration of mutual aid as a biological phenomenon. If the present concept of group and individual relationships in nature is not all sweetness and light, it is at least not untempered. The neo-Darwinians do not have everything their own way. The third, fourth, and fifth chapters of the *Descent of Man* will have their hearing.

It is necessary at this point to sketch something of the background and development of modern social theory. Not too much will be said of Darwin directly, for he had little to say explicitly on the subject. Yet his influence was revolutionary here, as in other sciences, and perhaps the reader may enjoy drawing his own conclusions as to just why this is true.

The structure and operation of human society is quite as pressing and practical a matter as the designing of buildings in which men may live and carry on their work. The nature of human society had received its good share of competent attention, so far back as the written record extends. Lucretius, to go no further into antiquity, describes in magnificent poetry the evolution of civilized society from savage beginnings. He wastes no time in talking of some aboriginal golden age, and he sweeps aside as nonsense the suggestion that some individual, say the Roman equivalent of Adam, had at some time consciously given names to everything about him.

Instead, Lucretius recounts the slow and painful development of the arts of fire, tool-making, housing, weaving, and speech. He describes the formation of social units—family and community—the beginnings of compassion, moral sense, and law. Moving on to a description of the rise of civilized empire, he notes the corrupting effects of wealth and luxury, the struggle for power in all its manifestations. Being a poet, he does not hesitate to pass moral judgments, or to suggest a remedy for the confusion that mankind has brought upon itself. There is no thought of return to an Arcadian paradise that never was. Instead, men are adjured to look on things with mind at peace, to live simply, and to know the true function of wealth. While the desire for more and better has led man upward, the struggle for power and possession can destroy him.

Here was an evolutionary account of society. It was based, as the poet admits, not on evidence but on his own intuitive reasoning. It is clear that he would much have preferred to have evidence. His concept of evolution does not degrade man—it makes man himself definitely responsible for the final outcome. But the Roman world of Lucretius did not, perhaps could not, heed his warning. Half a century after his death, Christ was born, taught with magnificent simplicity, and died tragically. In due time his followers assembled a body of Christian literature, but there was no place in it for such writings as those of the noble pagan poet. Hebrew tradition, with its account of Eden and the fall from innocence and grace, began to mold the social ideas of the western world, and has continued to do so. Thus man was enjoined by his highest faith, not to look back proudly on long ages of slow and painful achievement and to move onward to its refinement and perfection, but rather to beat himself over the head for what he had lost.

The very title of Darwin's book, the *Descent of Man,* reveals the subtle, pervasive influence of these ideas on the atmosphere of western thought. Darwin doubtless chose the word "descent," which literally means a climbing down, because it had become the standard term in genealogy. By delicate inference, man had moved downward from some lofty ancestral eminence. Of course Darwin, in using the word, had no such intent, any more than he might have wished to suggest that man had clambered down from his former abode in the trees. He simply took the word his culture provided, but the origin of that word speaks volumes for the unuttered assumptions of the culture. Hebrew influence was not the only element involved. Greeks and Romans both took great stock in a Golden Age, and ancestor worship was firmly grounded in the Orient. There was even a lively cult of the Golden Age in France, extending into the 18th century. Lucretius had really spoken for a small minority, and his lonely voice, for all its forthright courage, was drowned out.

So long as Western Christendom, over and above its conflicts, was in principle united into one Church, the structure and nature of its society could be conveniently accounted for. True, there had persisted from the days of Saxon paganism a thread of belief in consent and agreement as a basis for group living. Otherwise monarchy was, through appropriate certifying agencies, a divine institution and the order of society. Now the word "order" means a woven fabric. The weaver sets the loom and works the treadle. The design which appears is his, in its minutest detail, for threads and cloth are passive. There was no intellectual stimulus to look behind this assumption, and certainly no encouragement, so far as personal safety might be concerned. The practical difficulty of this conception was, of course, that it settled the question in advance. The moral difficulty lay in the fact that one might use it with equal facility to ascend to the City of God, or to descend into the dark recesses of Machiavelli's princely state. It left no room for the cleansing astringency of objective study.

The divine right of kings, like one of its last exponents, took an unconscionably long time to die, surviving the breakup of churchly unity. Pervasive and spectacular as they were, politics and war, kings and generals, took the eye of those who sought to analyze the character of society after it became safe to do so. Even today these matters continue to hypnotize both historian and reader. The humble arts of daily living, of communication, and of personal relations—all that we know now as culture—seemed too commonplace and too prosaic to be of great consequence. They were often well reported, as they had been earlier by Messer Marco Polo, but well into the 19th century they were regarded as being mainly amiable curiosities for the antiquarian or traveler. Few guessed that they were the very living stuff out of which society has grown.

Thus when the serious study of society began, as it did after the Revival of Learning, the emphasis was naturally upon institutions and conspicuous personalities. Hobbes, for example, saw the organic character of the State, while the 18th century French, probing into its mechanism, came up with the idea that it represented a kind of contract.

Inevitable it was that in such a period of social, political, economic, industrial and scientific ferment there should have been a deal of hard thinking on the problem of human society. Attention was not always centered on the most significant phenomena. True, high visibility usually guides the first steps of any science. The situation had its parallel in the biological science of the time, when microscopes were still crude and inefficient and the naturalist had before his naked eye countless objects to be investigated. And though Bacon had pointed out the inductive character of scientific evidence two centuries earlier, there was still plenty of confusion as to where valid proof left off and speculation began. Philosophers gave forth on social configuration and poets on social psychology.

So long as their views were recorded in black and white for future checking this was not too bad. At any rate, the vogue of predetermined answers was passing and that was a gain. Through the 18th and early 19th centuries, the idea of organic development and naturalism in society was gathering strength. Politics and economics were still lawfully bedded together as political economy. (Later they underwent a divorce of convenience from which they have been moving stealthily back to reunion.)

It was the political economists who began to analyze society with the microscope. The studies of Malthus on population were among the early fruits of their endeavor, and while Darwin's interest in social problems was incidental, he followed straight in this tradition. It is worth the trouble to reread Lucretius and the early chapters of Darwin's *Descent* at a sitting. Remembering the vast interval of time and human experience that separates them, they are remarkably alike. They have that profound compatibility which comes when men are struggling to get at the truth, and which melts away like beeswax when men are too sure they know the truth.

Darwin had seen something of primitive human cultures during the voyage of the *Beagle*. So had Huxley, who went in 1842 as surgeon and naturalist on H.M.S. *Rattlesnake*. Huxley's sketches and notes are excellent so far as they go, and while he was not always tolerant of native ways, he recognized that they were capable of rational explanation—a basic principle of modern anthropology. His expedition rescued a Mrs. Thompson who had been shipwrecked among the primitives near Cape York and had lived with them for some five years. Her descriptions of the wholesale slaughtering of infants among these people may well have remained in Huxley's mind when, in later years, he was pitted against the comfortable English gentlemen who were so resentful of Darwinism.

Literal believers in scripture, as Huxley's opponents professed themselves to be, held that because the guileless Adam had disobeyed an order, all subsequent men—some two billion of whom are alive today—have an inherent tendency to do evil rather than good. They further believed that, after a great flood had destroyed all of humanity except one family, whose descendants repeopled the earth, Ham, a son of this family, had violated a taboo by seeing the naked body of his drunken father. For that offense, Canaan, a son of Ham, was cursed and condemned to be a servant of servants to his brethren.

From the story of this curse the legend grew that the dark-skinned races of men were the descendents of Ham. It grew until ministers who preached the gospel of the compassionate Jesus of Nazareth were using it—in a land of printing-presses, steam railroads, and electric telegraphs—to justify negro slavery!

Suppose for a moment that the views of such gentlemen and their sympathizers had prevailed. The primitive Pacific islanders, living precariously near the limits of subsistence, would still be looked upon as living under a double curse—the sins of Adam and of Ham. In such an intellectual—not to say humanitarian—atmosphere, what kind of a science of man and society could there conceivably be? No wonder Huxley became impatient with his smug opponents—but not too impatient to dissect with cool and masterly skill some of the more egregious features of Hebrew and Christian tradition.

Herbert Spencer, for all his faith in science, must have lacked Darwin's humility towards evidence. He had preceded Darwin with a statement of belief in evolution. He was a hard and rigorous thinker. And he was interested in the study of society—a sociologist by profession. He went at the problem with conviction, and that was precisely the trouble. He was convinced in advance that the processes of society were to be explained in terms of the physical sciences, and as Professor Ellwood has pointed out, his influence on sociology has diminished with the years, while that of Darwin has grown. How could this be?

A recent analysis of American scientific personnel indicates strongly that the physicists are the cream of the intellectual crop, while the biologists are described as being largely "washed-out medical students"—an unkind category which certainly includes Darwin! No doubt Spencer would have won over Darwin in a modern intelligence test, at that, and perhaps handily. The point is, I think, that here exists a quality which, for lack of a better name, can be called biological sense, and which is more fairly tested by facing actual situations involving living organisms than by the usual type of intelligence test in which symbols play so large a part. It is not too important to know whether biological sense represents a higher or lower order of ability than the mathematical-physical sense. The two are not necessarily mutually exclusive. Biological phenomena are certainly the much more complex, much less susceptible to neat, compact solution. Whatever biological sense may be, Darwin had it, and Spencer did not. And just as the organisms which Darwin studied had a capacity for growth, so did his ideas.

Actually Spencer was on the track of an exceedingly important thing. The laws of matter and energy do operate in human society and in all communities of living organisms. This fact is basic to any intelligent program of conservation and economic justice. The French physiocrats had sensed it, and our technocrats were so near this truth that only their own ineptness and the alarm of their adversaries kept them from being effective. Henry Adams, as a young man in Europe, was fired by the social implications of the conservation of energy, which deserve far more attention than they have to this day received. But the trouble is that this viewpoint, in and of itself, tells little about the actual character of human society. It is something to be used after we have examined society on its own merits to see how it operates. This is a humdrum business of gathering commonplace facts. With what devilish fatality the most brilliant and able men have thought they could somehow avoid such a task and cut through direct to the truth!

Another pitfall in the road of social science was almost exactly paralleled in the history of medicine. As physicians have been concerned with the ills of the body, so humane students of society have naturally been interested in the ills of society. In both instances the short-cut seemed to be the obvious path. If one has to deal with disease, disease is the thing to study. Unfortunately, as we have already noted, it did not work that way in medicine. Not until attention was centered upon a better understanding of the structure and function of the normal, healthy human body did medical science really begin to advance.

We might, of course, make the morbid assumption that all societies are really pathological. Otherwise, we must study and understand the normal processes which operate to keep society going before we can do much about abnormal and unhealthy societies. Needless to say, this is probably the most intricate and difficult task that any science has ever faced. Yet it has been faced, and the influence of Darwin has been seen at its best in the resulting advance.

By common consent, the greatest benefit has come from the legitimizing of evolutionary thought. In this new light, society can be viewed as an organic process, not as something static. As much as anything can be in science, development may be taken for granted. Beyond this, however, the idea of selection has served as a powerful tool. Social systems, and the particular ways and institutions which operate within them, can be viewed as representing the survival of activities and relationships which have somehow worked well enough to fit the situation, and presumably have worked better than alternatives which must have been tried and discarded.

Applying this principle to the study of actual societies, we find that everything within them takes on new meaning. (It has become an axiom of technique that the worker must view any society from within.) When he does this, he discovers that each social group has its own consistent inner logic. This logic embraces its ways, from the most humble and routine of the domestic arts on up through the forms of belief and aesthetic expression. Religion, for example, no longer appears as a matter of capricious, misguided and erroneous credulity, but as an integral expression of, and sanction for, the whole process of living.

Following such a procedure and interpretation, students of human society have arrived at the concept of folk-ways, or culture patterns—one of the most useful and significant ideas of modern times. It is a remarkable fact that although the human body has not changed in essentials, the human species has moved across barriers of climate and topography, adjusting itself to a range and variety of conditions without precedent for any other form of life. It has accomplished what would be impossible without physical evolution in any other organism. And if we seek an explanation, we find it in culture. Man may modify his patterns of behavior in relation to the demands of new conditions of living. But man is a social being, as Darwin said. His patterns of behavior are learned patterns—conditioned responses. Whence are they learned, and to what are they conditioned? Obviously the behavior of the individual develops in relation to the ways and sanctions of his social group—the culture into which he is born.

To take some very simple illustrations, consider the different responses of a German and an American child to the sounds of "nine" or "hell," or to the word "hat." Or compare the reaction of a modern plowman with that of a Shawnee Indian of 1700 to a nodule of flint lying on the ground. To the plowman the flint is simply another stone, a hindrance to his plow and so to his livelihood. To the Indian it represents potential arrowheads or spear points—the means of defense or of getting food. No significant physical differences between people, no necessary differences in inherent mental capacity are here involved. The absolute physical quality of two sounds may be identical, the chemistry and physics of the flint remain the same in either instance, but the effects on human beings of different cultures are enormously different. Each has been conditioned by his culture.

And this brings us to a generalization of the first importance

—so simple as to be deceptive. What linked the Peruvian Indians to the steep Andean slopes for centuries, enabling them to sustain themselves on terraced fields where others would have perished or moved away in a few generations? What has forced the relatively literate American farmer to abandon the gentler slopes of New England which are now reverting to forest? What has kept the boundary between the United States and Canada, some three thousand miles in length, the occasion for nothing much more serious than the confiscation of occasional fish-nets or the apprehension of a smuggler now and then during a century when the Rhine between France and Germany has thrice run red with blood?

It is a lazy answer, and a wrong one, to explain these contrasts in terms of wisdom or folly, good or evil, simply. Rather the answer is to be sought in the process called culture. It is through this process that mankind, in all its variant social groups, is related to the physical environment, and each individual and group to its fellows. In the varying forms of human culture, we find both the instrument and the expression of social process.

THE OBJECTION might reasonably be raised, at this point, that Darwin's personality and the details of his contribution have been kept in the background. For example, Darwin put forward, in his later life, the idea that tiny physical entities are given off by every portion of the living organism, then diffused throughout the body. Recombining, notably in the sex cells, they influence the development of the new individual, each acting upon its appropriate organ or structure. This idea he called "a provisional theory of pangenesis" and few of his suggestions have been more roughly treated.

Darwin was, of course, insisting primarily that some physical explanation of the continuity of life and development must be possible. And because he pushed hard on his particular hypothesis he has been accused of conduct unbecoming a scientist. The reverse is probably true, for it is often necessary, in testing a provisional hypothesis, to push it to the limit, until it either prevails or breaks down, on the evidence. It is easy to forget the essential point—that he called the idea "provisional."

It is easy, too, to forget that science is not served merely by those who are technically and completely "right." It is served equally, and at times more effectively by those who are simply explicit—who offer a clean-cut thesis that can be tested, without ambiguity, for what it is worth. Darwin's gemmules, or pangenes, are forgotten. But we do have the hormones—chemical messengers they are called—that regulate growth and other processes, and the genes within the chromosomes that control heredity and thus regulate the pattern of hormonal activity. The fundamental idea, that there must be physical units through which these processes operate, has been brilliantly redeemed.

From first to last, Darwin's pronouncements cover a wide range of technical problems. Each judgment of his has had to take its chances in the subsequent trial by ordeal that science is. Some have fared well, others worse, just as some of the injunctions of a parent lodge in the character of a child, while others go unheeded, and still others produce a contrary reaction. It is the residual, or essential quality of the influence then, that is our concern. If we seem to have kept Darwin in the background, we have not forgotten his majestic presence there.

He is solidly in the background, too, though in a curiously neglected way, of the subject with which this chapter deals. He was a great pioneer in a field of science which had not even been named when he wrote the *Origin*. That field has to do with life in all its interrelations with environment, and is called *Ecology*. Darwin called himself a naturalist and would have been surprised at any other designation—at least until the world, by common consent, called him a philosopher. But he was certainly an ecologist and one of the greatest. For his work has made it impossible, except as a provisional device, ever again to think of life as something apart from environment.

His work made ecology inevitable, as it did genetics. Both sciences rest squarely upon his pioneering work, and neither could do without it, in theory or in practice. Yet the debt of ecology to Darwin is seldom acknowledged in words—a curious situation, in truth, which anyone can verify for himself for the trouble of examining the indexes of a few books.

Thoughtful students of natural history, from Theophrastus and Herodotus down through von Humboldt, had been concerned with some of the effects of environment upon organisms. A few had observed the effects which organisms have upon environment. True, environment had to be described in pretty rough fashion—not too unlike the familiar Jackass Barometer, "When the tail is wet it is raining, when it is dry, the weather is fair." Yet in spite of the lack of accurate measurements, men had a shrewd and sensible conception of the march of the seasons, the distribution of moisture and sunshine, and the critical limits of temperature. Those who had traveled widely knew something of the variations of climate, and even the stay-at-homes realized what differences there could be in soils, slopes, drainage and altitude. It was clear, too, that these matters affected the distribution of plant and animal life. The gatherer knew where to look for wild fruits and roots, the hunter where to search for his game. And presently the grower, by a ceaseless process of trial and failure, re-trial and success, began to learn where and how he could make the earth yield most generously to his wishes.

Any fool could tell a wood from a heath, or a swamp from a copse or thicket of shrubs. The various types of vegetation had their names in folk-speech, as did many of the plants which composed them and the animals which chose them for abode. Men did not look for figs on thistles or for frogs on dry hilltops. What more was necessary?

One swallow does not make a spring, nor one tree make a forest. But when the swallows come to stay, spring is at hand. When tree stands beside tree, in dense array, we have the wood. This seems simplicity itself. One has only to add, individual upon individual, to get the sum, and so to get the world of nature, the living landscape with its plants and animals. No wonder that the underlying fact of organization was missed.

True, the traveling von Humboldt, like others before and after him, wrote of many kinds of forests and treeless places filled with strange plants, of grassy plains and weird deserts. A rational anatomy and physiology had begun to sense something of the amazing fitness of organisms for their varied and special conditions of life. Men were aware of certain deep compatibilities and antagonisms in nature, and even of certain indispensable relationships between species. Mostly these were on the basis of food, but not entirely so.

> "Out of the dead came forth the living,
> Out of the strong came forth the sweet,
> Out of the eater came forth meat."

The mistletoe required the oak, and the delicate fern the grateful shade of the cool, gray beech tree.

Yet the prevailing concept of living nature was in its essence that of an arithmetical sum. There was little notion of the elaborate and seamless web of mutual needs and compulsions which operate throughout nature. Thus it was that when Christian Conrad Sprengel in 1793 published his account of the intricate interrelationships of insects and flowers, under the imaginative title *The Secret of Nature Discovered*, the work was coldly ignored and remained in an oblivion from which it was finally rescued by Charles Darwin. Thus far can men be misled by their blind assurance that two and two always make four, no more, no less.

It is not surprising, if we consider what static and wooden ideas men had regarding their own social patterns, that they understood the patterns of wild nature even more dimly. One simply puts a garden together and there it is. What is living nature but a wilder, unweeded garden, a sum of all its parts? And we must remember that the hand of man had lain heavily on western Europe. Even its forests were more park than wilderness.

We know now that the woodsmen surveyors in the New World had their moments of insight. We find here and there in their notes such an observation as "here the kinds of trees seem to be changing"—an intimation of process and dynamic development. Before the 19th century was very far along, the naturalists of Europe, already interested in what they called the geography of plants, began to see more clearly that the fens and forests, glades and marshes, of their own familiar countryside were representations of a kind of social order. A few even spoke of the development or life history of such living communities.

Actually this is something anyone can see for himself by taking trouble to watch an abandoned field for a few years. It is a phenomenon so universal, so simple, so close at hand, that one wonders, after he has learned of it, how anyone with half an eye could have failed to note it. We call it succession today, and the idea has become one of the most useful tools in our kit.

Before the 19th century had ended, the organic character of living communities was an accepted fact. The youthful landscape of Scandinavia, not long abandoned by its cover of glacial ice, is pitted and varied, full of sharp, clean contrasts of topography, with vegetation to fit. Its streams are young and actively developing, its myriad lakes are slowly filling as all lakes must, for lakes are born to die. Here within an area so restricted that one did not have to consider different climates were varied social groups of plants and animals, and all stages of them. The landscape was like a series of time-lapse photographs from which one might justly and reasonably reconstruct the course of ceaseless activity.

It was in such surroundings that the first work to be known as plant ecology was done. But its implications clearly extended to animals. Indeed the word ecology had already been coined by the zoologist Haeckel. For the zoologists had found, in the very practical business of investigating the oyster crop, that they could only deal with this problem by viewing the oyster as one of the many organisms in a complex marine community. One does not think of the oyster as a social being. By proverb he is the antithesis. Yet there is in fact no other basis for interpreting his ways. Let us not forget, moreover, that all of this work went on after Darwin had voiced the unity of nature and the interdependence of living organisms.

While communities in miniature were thus being viewed, plant geography on the world scale was likewise enjoying the benefits of the Darwinian release. This farflung discipline had gained a new dimension—that of time—and with it a firm bond with historical geology. It became, in fact, an exciting field of study, and so it remains to this day.

The presence of plants—and of course animals—in any particular place was now, under the evolutionary idea, a challenge to first-rate detective work. How widely did a given species range, what conditions did it require, what were its nearest relatives, and where were they to be found? How long ago had it been isolated from its kin on other continents by sea or desert or mountain range? All of these questions and a score of others cried for answer. And each answer, as it was obtained, suggested new and equally intriguing problems. It was like the midwestern game of tracing families back to the seaboard, thence across the Atlantic to their ancestral homes in Europe. But it was a cleaner form of sport, unmarred by fake records and appeals to vanity.

The peculiar adaptations which fitted organisms to such special environments as desert or rainforest now came up for more serious and businesslike attention too, for were they not the very instruments and evidence of natural selection? And with this new zeal came a more absorbing interest in the habits and structures whereby organisms were fitted for binding interrelations with other species. The tropics, richest reservoir of life, afforded an unending pageant of biological curiosities which were turned to good solid intellectual account, while the familiar and prosaic temperate regions proved themselves a far more alluring ground for inquiry than anyone had supposed them to be.

Most important of all, perhaps, was a new conception of such great reaches of plant and animal life as the forest, the steppe, and the desert, each embracing within itself a host of local variants. These great formations—for so they came to be called—were now viewed as magnificent functional entities, great continental communities, each composed of a hierarchy of lesser communities. And each formation was seen as reflecting and integrating the great zones of climate more sensitively, more accurately, and more completely than any instruments yet devised by man. This fact had to be established, of course, by an infinite amount of detailed and conscientious work, but the end result was enough to fire any poet. In a sense, here was a high and solid plateau of scientific achievement, confirming as it did the universality of genetic process and the unity of the natural world in the greatest assemblages of living organisms as well as in the least, in communities no less than in individuals and species.

What this new viewpoint meant for our understanding of the world of living nature may be guessed from a comparison. No one questions the value and importance of a city directory. But no one would pretend, either, that it gives us much insight into the character of the city. For that purpose we must have a functional analysis of the community itself, showing the social processes which are at work and their interplay whose resultant is the whole. For this purpose the directory would be little more than a point of beginning, and the same is true of the invaluable species lists which once seemed a sufficient record of the wild communities of nature.

City and forest, village and marsh, are more, too, than systems of current, contemporary activity. All are expressions of a past, and none are to be understood except in those terms. Why is Cincinnati famed for its music and its parks, Cleveland for its civic spirit? The historical factor, as it is called, has become indispensable to the interpretation of the living landscape.

Little patches of prairie, complete with bluestem grass, rattlesnakes, and western insects, were found studding the wooded expanse of Ohio. They seem strangely out of place in that forest climate until we invoke the historical factor. So doing, and following out a handful of clues, we discover these prairies to be the lingering vestiges of a climate much warmer and dryer than the present. And we find, as we follow the threads of evidence, that the retreat of the glacial ice was not so simple an event as had been supposed. A series of climatic episodes, of retreat and advances, seems to have been involved, with marked effects on vegetation, soil, and, as doubtless we shall find, on the communities of primitive man.

The weathering of rock into soil—a process initiated by lichens—and the gradual invasion of living organisms into lifeless areas was understood in some measure before Darwin's time. Emerson in 1841 had written of ". . . patient periods . . . before . . . the rock is broken and the first lichen race has disintegrated the thinnest external plate into soil, and opened the door for the remote Flora, Fauna, Ceres, and Pomona to come in."

Darwin himself, in his classic study on earthworms, had shown something of the dynamics of soil, for he reported that these tireless animals brought up to the surface enough material to make three inches of topsoil in a century. Chemistry had traced the unceasing round of use and reuse of many of the elements, while Darwin's austere contemporary, Pasteur, was making possible the study of microorganisms which are such an indispensable part of the soil's activities. From many sources, and not the least from Charles Darwin's own experiments, were gathering the materials for a revolutionary view of soil as an expression of genetic process. One may today, in fact, quite acceptably speak of soil as a process—a logical extension of Darwin's greater premises with regard to the unity and continuity of nature.

Yet the older, more static ideas have a curious vitality, and are to be found even in books of recent imprint. The seeds of a modern soil science, like those of genetics, lay dormant until toward the end of the 19th century. Then, by one of those happy coincidences so frequent in science, Russian scholars and American, working independently on soils which had not been disturbed by human activity, discovered that soil was far more than a mechanical-chemical mixture, the favorable seat of biological activities. It was instead the outcome of a highly integrated process involving realms inorganic and organic, lifeless and living, the energy of sun, forces atmospheric and geological. Under any given set of conditions that would support life, its components tended to adjust themselves into a more and more highly organized system. As this development proceeded, the capacity of the soil to sustain life increased until an equilibrium was reached. And the history of a soil so generated was to be read from its profile—a vertical section from surface down into parent material.

Aside from being an immensely practical discovery, which it was, this new view of the soil was a bold confirmation of the inseparability of life and environment. For the roots and worms and rodents, the fungi and bacteria, which we had been accustomed to think of as *living in* the soil were now to be viewed as part and parcel of it. Without their presence and activity the soil would not be what it is—would not properly be soil at all.

From the beginnings of agriculture and herding, men had often been obliged to abandon the lands which their fathers had found flowing with milk and honey, and this tragedy has continued with infinite repetition to the present. There was much talk of soil exhaustion after chemistry emerged from alchemy, and a few of the earlier geologists who, like Lyell, had their eyes opened to the unceasing activity of wind and water, knew that the destructive forces of nature could remove soil. Some traditions of husbandry, as in Peru and Pennsylvania, seemed to safeguard the soil. More did not, but nothing much was done until the closing of the American frontier and the occupation of all available virgin areas.

Then a combination of events and the evangelistic fervor of a handful of scientists suddenly dramatized the problem. In a world already overpopulated, much of it underfed, with a daily net gain of some 50,000 human beings and a daily loss of an equal number of acres of soil, the earth beneath our feet suddenly took on new and terrifying importance. One of the first and most practical problems was to make mankind appreciate what soil is and what it means, not only to the man who owns and works with it, but to the urbanite who, though remote, is no less dependent upon it.

Here is economics in the raw. Civilized man, at the peak of his scientific and intellectual progress, finds that his material destiny is inseparable from that of this dark and silent carpet with which Nature had clothed the earth before his advent. That carpet, the soil, is the product of prolonged and highly integrated activity, and he himself, Lord of the Earth, is caught in the process too!

Much has been written and said of these matters in the past two decades. Old Malthus is dug up daily and elaborately buried again. Charge and countercharge, rebuttal and denial, flit back and forth. Sober judgment is difficult, but we need not linger here to consider just how serious man's plight may be. We may only be sure, with Sir John Russell, that man will continue to pay with sweat and vigilance for the privilege of remaining alive.

Our present concern is with the fact that a turning point has been reached in our insatiate use of science. We have been content to apply the findings of science to ease our burdens, to make living more convenient and luxurious, to heal our bodies, and to postpone our inevitable deaths. We have used science eagerly to add to our material wealth (at whatever cost to the sources) and to intensify our food production. And we have gone serenely ahead, in peace and war, confident that science can rescue us from any jam, no matter how bad it is. We have modern technology at our service. But our bodies are stone-age bodies, if as good, our minds no better than the Greek, and our morals the patchy product of a long and checkered past. Above all, we must eat, a vulgar necessity whose rules were in operation a billion years ago.

We are in truth at a turning point. Shall we continue to use science for our more immediate needs, as a sort of glorified house-boy or handyman, while we let the future take care of itself? Or are we at length in a mood to hear the truth about ourselves, to take science into our confidence, have it examine the books whose pages should be captioned—Man, Debtor . . . Environment, Creditor—in stalwart double entry? In plain words, are we ready to see ourselves for a moment through the wise, compassionate, and troubled eyes that peered out beneath the bushy brows and massive forehead of Charles Darwin?

Can the dead past bury its dead? The past seems very much alive in us all. We are reminded often enough that the business of evolution is now in our own hands. I suspect that most of us, confronted with such a challenge, would much prefer to go fishing. Of those who did not, a goodly number might bear watching, for the love of power is a poisonous thing. The issue of evolution is in world politics in grimmer fashion than Bryan ever dreamed it would be. But the helping hand of deliberate time will surely work with us if we simply live our lives in a reasonably honest understanding of the kind of world in which we are. If we have this understanding, our choices and our actions will shape themselves in its light. The problem lies deeper than mere knowledge, of course. But right knowledge is the beginning of wisdom, and wisdom once gained brings its own powerful sanctions.

The physical sciences have placed vast stores of energy and a multitude of new materials and devices in our hands. Yet we must be on the eve of a still mightier challenge. He that ruleth himself is greater than he that taketh a city. A society that has the measure of itself is greater than one which chains the lightnings and harnesses the seas. It may be that we shall presently begin to use science in a new and worthier way, to give us our bearings, to help us understand the ecology of our own species.

To this end we must weave together all that we know of ourselves and of the physical world. We have fruitfully pursued knowledge to the smallest knowable constituents of matter, even to the mysterious bridge between matter and energy. At the other extreme we have studied the most complex manifestations of matter and energy in the living community. Our challenge now is to a new and grand synthesis, a new unity between these extremes of knowledge.

It is no trick to convince a hard-headed industrialist that the men who design machinery for him must respect the principles of conservation of energy, and that his chemical engineers must not do violence to the laws of mass action and equilibrium. In the field of finance, he knows that his accountants, the analysts of business, must be able to classify the flow of organized energy and material which we call wealth into such categories as assets, liabilities, depreciation, income and expense. He knows that the stability of his whole enterprise depends upon the realism and insight with which this analysis is conducted.

What he does not realize (and this is true for most of us) is that these same fundamental principles operate throughout the world of experience, in the widest communities of living organisms and their environments, and in human society as the highest component of the world community. Withhold the energy of sunshine, or the carbon, phosphorus, or water from a continent and its life will cease—at all levels. And as a chain is no stronger than its weakest link, if any one of half a hundred of the requisite conditions for abundant life be too scantily met, by so much will the capacity of a landscape, measured by the communities upon it, be reduced. The unique qualities of life, even of human life, do not supersede the physical verities, but are built out of them. This fact we ignore at our peril.

And if we carry our synthesis of the physical and biological still further, we shall indubitably find that the origin, development and maturity of living communities are in accord with the physical laws which govern process. Whether we consider a sweetened cup of tea, a moving automobile, a field of corn, or a civilization, we are viewing a system whose irresistible tendency is *toward* equilibrium, balance, and economy of the energy which flows through it. As we work consciously with this principle, we create. As we work, consciously or in ignorance, in violence to it, we destroy. We can, in very truth, keep books on our great enterprise of living on this earth, provided we have an honest understanding of these fundamental rules.

Grand, comprehensive and illuminating as Darwin's conception of evolution is, it comes to its fullest fruit only when we see it as an expression of the great principle of dynamic equilibrium. Our highest opportunity for eventual human freedom and dignity lies precisely in the fact that we are the products of evolution. As responsible units in the great web of life, we can be guided by an infinitely long inherited experience, built into our bodies and minds and shaping our decisions in the interest of our own species.

If we are true to our largest measure of understanding, we need not fail.

FAITH AND LEARNING

ON MAY 25, 1925, a young high school instructor, John Thomas Scopes, was arrested in Rhea County, Tennessee, on the charge of unlawfully teaching the theory of evolution in the public schools—an action specifically forbidden by the statutes of that sovereign state. There was no question that he had done violence to the law. The judge, sworn to uphold the law, had no choice. The verdict was guilty, but the incident became a *cause celèbre,* rivalling in public interest the Dreyfus trial.

The aging William Jennings Bryan came to aid the prosecution. This was to be his final public activity. His testimony was taken but not admitted to the jury; neither was that of the eminent scientists who offered themselves in opposition. Clarence Darrow of Chicago volunteered his service as attorney for the defense and in that capacity cross-examined Bryan with devastating effect, for Bryan had no understanding of biology and no conception of the vast sweep of time involved in evolution. One of his arguments on the lecture platform had been, "If man is descended from the monkeys, why cannot we go into Africa today and see monkeys turning into men?" He felt, too, that evolution was discredited by the admission of scientists that individual civilized men had no greater capacity than ancients or primitives.

The British, who had long since accepted evolution as a matter of course, and whose Lambeth Conference of the Anglican Communion was later to announce that it had no objections to the doctrine, were both amazed and amused by the trial. The newspapers had a carnival, and American scientists were up in arms.

Four years earlier, while the storm against evolution was still brewing, William Bateson, in many respects the intellectual successor of Darwin, had been brought from England to address the American Association for the Advancement of Science. Edward L. Rice, an able zoologist and sincere Christian, had published in 1925 a carefully reasoned paper, "Darwin and Bryan—a Study in Method," showing the shallowness of the anti-evolution attack. But the tide at the time was running otherwise. Protestantism (whose more enlightened wing had sponsored the teaching of science at countless small liberal arts colleges in the United States) was in the grip of a powerful reaction. One of the most conspicuous fruits of this reaction was the 18th amendment to the Constitution, forbidding the sale of alcoholic beverages. Thus evangelical Christianity, at the peak of its power, used the advantage to pass sumptuary, and where possible, antievolution laws. As though one could, or should, legislate into literal truth a beautiful, symbolic poem—the early chapters of Genesis!

In 1884, forty-one years before the Scopes trial, the Rev. Dr. James Woodrow, then a teacher in the South Carolina College and Theological Seminary, had been brought to trial and convicted of heresy for teaching evolution "with undue sympathy for the Darwinian school," in contravention of the scriptural account of creation. But the higher Presbyterian authorities refused to sustain the verdict and Dr. Woodrow moved on to fame and greater influence. He was, incidentally, an uncle of Woodrow Wilson.

Very different, in several respects, was the first great conflict on evolution in the United States—the battle between Asa Gray and Louis Agassiz, both professors at Harvard. Neither was trying to unseat the other as a teacher and so deprive him of his livelihood. Both men were familiar with the evidence and competent to discuss it. Like the Civil War then raging and eclipsing their debate, their war was one between gentlemen.

Then, too, the rancor of conservative religious beliefs was mitigated in this instance. Harvard had long since been given up by the ardent evangelicals as a hopeless Unitarian nest—one of the reasons for Amherst's being founded was to counteract its "poison." Neither man was attacking religion. Gray, the champion of evolution, was personally devout, scholarly and intelligent to boot—an impregnable combination in 19th century New England. He carried the day at Harvard and in the wider world of science. But the great hinterland of America, where religion and higher education were still firmly wedded, had not yielded.

In a sense, the congregationalism of New England and the episcopalianism of the early South represented two poles of approach, each influencing the other faiths in its vicinity. The congregational school had a great mind to forge its faith as it went along. If the breast-plate cramped the righteous, back it went into the fire to be reworked until it fit. By contrast, the episcopalian group (and its more vigorous evangelical successors in the South) regarded its armor as heirloom, not to be marred or meddled with. Regardless of rattling joints or pinched flesh, it was to be donned and worn into battle just as it had been when last hung on the pegs.

Where the first of these tendencies prevailed, education was logically a business of teaching the young to think and giving them, according to their capacities, materials to use in that difficult process. Common schools came as a matter of course. So did higher schools to train teachers, lay and ecclesiastic.

Where the more conservative mood was in the ascendancy, those who had the leisure for learning and reflection were more or less indoctrinated in what to think. A great number were not encouraged to think at all, or even given much to think about, beyond the trials and simple joys which were their daily lot. And so the schools, high and low, were largely for those who could afford them. Let it be clear that this second mood was not conceived in malice. It had its own dignity, even its high ethical obligation. Leadership was a serious matter, equal to generous sacrifice, if occasion required. Nor was the contrasting mood always innocent of everything mean, sordid and destructive.

As the great interior of the continent was invaded, both traditions moved westward in spotty and straggling fashion. Many individuals escaped from the formal restraints of any sectarian control. Strong, even violent, means were required to recapture such fugitives from faith. Frontier revivals were legendary. Many a parent of today who fancies himself shocked by the new generation would be put *hors de combat* by a day with his ancestors along the Ohio river or in the piney woods—just as others might be unexpectedly charmed by a similar experience, of course. Faith diffused and land was colonized by varied kinds, in varied ways, though the evangelistic spirit was strong. The earlier church schools often taught reading and the later public schools often taught prayers and the Bible. But in the background the two moods we have described were persistent and by no means wholly regional or even denominational, coming to grips in more than one community, while education hung poised on the issue.

Over the land sprang up colleges dedicated, almost without exception, to the greater glory of God and the training of His ministers. Doctors and lawyers could be trained by apprenticeship and their own efforts. Preachers and their lay counterparts, teachers, were expected to have some formal learning. True, some sects were willing to ordain any who had the "call," but even these groups soon recognized the value of discipline, most conveniently administered by academic means.

The curricula of these young colleges were in the English tradition, tight and classical. Yet science was tolerated for several reasons. It made manifest the Creator's plans. It was a source of useful information to leaders bound for primitive territory. And it gave some knowledge of natural history, useful after 1859, in dealing with the skeptical and the troubled, whose literal faith had been threatened by the new doctrine of evolution. Thus one of the "settees" in a young midwestern college was occupied by a professor who taught physiology, chemistry, botany, and later some geology. This man was a physician, but many of the early teachers were ordained ministers.

Mathematics and Newtonian astronomy could give no trouble—were indeed canonical as we know from Addison's glorious hymn, "The spacious firmament on high." Natural philosophy, that is to say, chemistry and physics, could be kept under control. Geology was more troublesome, but by granting that the Biblical day was sufficiently long and invoking the deluge rather freely when fossils were at issue, a believer could deal with it. Even so, there was the instance of Alexander Winchell. An active and eminent geologist, he was trained at a church-sponsored college and fought the extension of land-grant public institutions. Yet in 1878, after three years at Vanderbilt University, he found himself in trouble for advocating the theory of evolution and teaching the existence of pre-Adamite man. He offered to resign if the trustees would put on record the reasons for their opposition. This they refused to do, abolishing his chair instead.* The University of Michigan took him back at once.

Biology was decidedly an afterthought in the curricula of early American colleges, except for small doses of human physiology and a little polite botany. Serious laboratory instruction was rare until the 1880's, and for a long time thereafter was snubbed and penalized by the divines, the classicists and the humanists, who were in the seats of power.

Meanwhile tax-supported universities and colleges, of which Georgia founded in 1801 and Virginia in 1819 were the prototypes, were rapidly getting under way. They had no sectarian commitments, yet religious influences were frequently strong at the beginning and sometimes persistent. Science was essential for technical training and research in these state universities. Graduates of church colleges, polished off by study in Europe, or at older Eastern universities, and presently at Johns Hopkins, found themselves in a seller's market for scientists. This was a tonic to the smaller institutions, which thereupon proceeded, out of all proportion to their size, to contribute to the vigorous scientific life of the nation as they still do. Under these circumstances, only the more obscure and inferior colleges have made much of an

* Though Bishop McTyeire took great pains to show Winchell that there was no parallel between his case and that of Galileo, he also told Winchell that his ideas were "contrary to the plan of redemption." Cardinal Bellarmin had told Galileo that his ideas "vitiated the plan of salvation." A. D. White to D. C. Gilman, Paris, July 24, 1878. Gilman MSS. Johns Hopkins University.

issue of evolution against orthodox belief. In the better liberal arts colleges, the influence of resident scientists has profoundly modified the old, rigid, religious conceptions and acted as a general leaven. The humanistic training of their scientific graduates has likewise helped to offset the effects of narrow technical specialization and the scientific dogmatism which is its earmark.

Thus in dramatic course has evolution been naturalized and largely assimilated into faith and learning. There is still a vigorous fundamentalist movement, by no means entirely at the lower intellectual levels, though mostly so. Much of it can be traced to the neglect by powerful churches of the poor, ignorant and unchurched in their own communities, who thus fall readily into the hands of a rude and fiery evangelism based on literal truth of scripture. Such raw faiths give at least a measure of form and color to drab lives. The Church of Rome has, with some notable exceptions, managed the problem of evolution with prudence and dignity, avoiding *ex cathedra* judgment, and chiefly reserving its own opinion as to the origin of the human soul.

But evolution has been much more than a passive guest, finally made welcome. We have seen its powerful influence on biological and social science. It has done no less for religion and educational doctrine and practice. By infusing the study of religion itself it has thrown that subject into new clarity. Whatever this has cost by its effect on cherished forms of belief will, in the end, be richly repaid. For we know enough now of the evolution of religions to see behind their multiformity this fact—that religion in some form can no more be dispensed with than the human skin can be spared from the body.

Sages can repeat, with variations, that if there be no God, it becomes necessary to invent one. So saying, they suggest, but do not touch, a profound truth. Every human culture, and every individual within it more directly, has its conception of the kind of universe of which it is a part. And upon that conception and the emotional values which go with it, conduct is based. Men think, and act, and feel, to fit the kind of reality which they believe encompasses them. This, no more, no less, is religion. It may be conceived in ignorance or enlightenment, in crassness or exquisite sensibility, embroidered with elaborate invention or starkly simple —but there it is, an ultimate embodiment of group and individual values. And if this view of it be correct, its very basis lies in those matters upon which humanity can achieve the highest degree of accord and upon which it can build as a common foundation, no matter how much the several superstructures may diverge in form and quality.

It is just here that science takes on its greatest significance for mankind. Not that it is in any sense omniscient, or ever can be; but that, within its expanding limits, it is a source of agreement. Only by consensus does science grow. Each new discovery must be reported and tested before it becomes a part of our common understanding. Religion deals with much that is beyond the present reach of science, yet there is a growing acceptance of the fact that faith has much to gain and nothing to lose by squaring itself at the start with the physical and biological verities. These things can be universal for human experience. The practical importance of sharing them is very great, is in fact becoming crucial. Who shall say what the human spirit may gain thereby? We have no firmer argument for the brotherhood of man than the fact of our common descent.

For forty years after the *Origin* appeared there was little change in schools below the college level. Science was gradually introduced, but the three R's in elementary school and conventional subjects in high school prevailed. Bookkeeping and drafting might be offered. In 1885 an excellent teacher of mathematics and Latin could be reproved for begging that a workshop be set up for some of her boys—good boys—whose brains were mostly in their fingers. But by 1900 the United States was becoming, so far as population was concerned, urban rather than rural. Schools were beginning to strain at the seams, and have been crowded ever since. Industrialism had brought immigration so that large numbers of first and second generation of foreign born had to be reckoned with. The practices and postulates of American education, which had been fairly simple, were up for re-examination.

And here the evolutionary doctrine of Darwin came into its own as a social force.

Sumner and others had applied Darwinism, or their conception of it, to the world of business and affairs, seeing the forces of competition as a kind of justifiable natural selection. But there was also a group of men who were looking more deeply into the contemporary scene, searching for some evidence of underlying principles and social process that would square with new notions of the natural world.

One can explain rather simply, if he does not mind being superficial, what happened. Two American philosophers—both of them psychologists as well—rose to great influence at a time when changing social pressures in the schools were intense and the school population was growing beyond all precedent. Both of these men were interested in education. Both were associated with great universities which trained many teachers. The demand for teachers had suddenly become enormous, and one of these universities set up a large college designed, as one famous but bewildered Danish visitor put it, "to teach teachers to teach teachers to teach." ("Never in my life before have I seen anything like it!" he mourned.)

The leverage they brought to bear upon American education is obvious, nor was it lessened by the commercial enterprise of the text-book industry, now Big Business. Moreover, there was in the making, like the branches of a distributary stream or river system in reverse, a flood of teachers' colleges in the various states. Through these institutions the new philosophy and its ancillary techniques could be piped to the classrooms of the nation, not always, of course, in their pristine purity. When the history of this new system is some day written, boldly and fairly, it will reveal the most amazing mixture of devoted public service, political humbuggery, humane zeal, exploitation, hard, honest thinking, and intellectual fraud that can be imagined. Since education is the greatest of our public enterprises next to the waging of wars, and is subject to a mixture of state and local control, this should not perhaps be too surprising.

What may be called the technical side of education, the art and philosophy of the teacher, is still shaking under the impact of evolution. This is not to imply that teachers have risen above Socrates or the early Jesuits (as the modern physician soars above even the greatest of the ancient healers by virtue of professional knowledge) or that they ever will. Psychology has helped, of course. But it is still doubtful whether the best teachers of today owe much more of their craftsmanship to psychology than, say, the best of our painters to a knowledge of the spectrum and the chemistry of pigments. Yet we certainly have a generally better understanding of the developing mind, the physiology of learning and—what is supremely useful for our system of compulsory public education—a much clearer understanding of individual differences than did older generations. And we have a repertoire of mass production devices.

William James and John Dewey must be reckoned as great men, chief translators of Darwinism and its corollaries into the structure of American thought. It is dangerous to label philosophers, still more dangerous to group them, but both by their own admission were pragmatists, holding that the truth is to be tested in action. Like the tree and the vine, the truth is to be known by its fruit, although a captious botanist might note that the fruit of a plant is only one of many criteria by which it may be judged and identified. The influence of natural selection is evident in pragmatism. If a thing works, it survives. If it will not work, out it goes. Extended to ideas, an idea that will not work, isn't so. Extended to the business of education, pragmatism implied experiment and a general loosening up of that hitherto very tight process. Spencer and Huxley, the latter certainly a very great teacher, had long since tried to pry education open on the strictly utilitarian basis that all knowledge was not of equal value, that much was being taught that had outlived its usefulness, and a great deal that is vital to modern life was being neglected. With this James and Dewey would agree, but they shifted out onto larger ground—the nature of the educational process and its relation to the whole process of human society.

Both James and Dewey had derived the idea of pragmatism from Charles Peirce, a philosopher who was obliged to die in order to be given his due. Now Peirce, who had one of the clearest minds ever to grace this continent, believed that action, or specific and visible effect, is not the final test of truth but a working method of *moving toward* the truth. His philosophy of education was compressed into one sentence. *A teacher must understand the logic of his subject and the psychology of his pupil.* It is abundantly clear from his now published writings that Peirce viewed the logic of a subject not merely as a something internal to it, but as something which involves its relation to all of human knowledge and experience as well. And he must similarly have viewed the psychology of the student in its relation to the culture in which that student was living.

James and Dewey were in direct contact with leaders of education. Peirce was not. James is easy to read, Dewey difficult. Both are difficult to understand, and for good reason. The new dynamic, evolutionary picture of the universe could not be strait-jacketed into the traditionally neat pattern of any of the older systems of knowledge. Peirce put it perfectly when he said he had only once felt the glow of true praise—when an opponent criticized him for not seeming to be absolutely certain of what he did believe. Thus the very sources to which American education chose to look for guidance were tentative, and in the painful stages of growth. The prospects were magnificent, but the outlines blurred and details not always distinct.

Clearly, however, pragmatism justified an experimental approach in education, and called for it. But the planning and execution of such experiments was to be placed in the hands of those who were at best several removes from the sources of inspiration. To the initial uncertainties of the new philosophy were added the uncertainties of zealous interpreters, too often inclined to formulate dicta and utter war cries, thus playing false their own avowed principles.

Add to this the fact that experiment in education is a very different matter from experiment in the natural sciences. The economy of experiment over ordinary trial and error is that the cost of failure—always a possibility to be reckoned with—is so much less. Education is not starting from scratch. It has been through a long process of trial and error in the past, and as it stands today is a fair expression of natural selection. There has been a survival of the better, more efficient practices. The objects of educational experiment are human beings, and with them the price of failure comes high. Under the circumstances, a philosophy based on natural selection ought logically to have considerable respect for the past and its achievements, to rely on scrutiny and selection at least as fully as on experiment, and above all to avoid the error of throwing baby out with the soapy bath water.

In consequence of these things, the present state of American education is not a little confused. Pre-school and elementary teaching have unquestionably gained, because of an increased concern for, and understanding of, child development. More thought than ever before is being given to the large group whose needs and talents do not fit the traditional systems. Perhaps this is being done at the cost of those of superior endowment. At any rate a strong reaction is under way. Harvard, which not only loosened up its system, but removed the bolts by adopting a system of free electives, is now trying to restore some semblance of unity and form, and the tendency is growing.

At the extreme there is a neo-classicism, outdoing the old by its emphasis on great books of the past, and so discarding all of the economies of effort which the past has found so necessary in education. There are good and valid reasons why schools had given up, for example, the teaching of mathematics from Newton's own treatises. Granted without argument that contact with first-rate, creative minds is supremely desirable, those who wish to restore form to education might well have bent their energies toward the development of modern textbooks with distinction of style, breadth and profundity of scholarship; and toward the recruiting of high intelligence for the teaching profession. So long as an able man, in order to choose *freely* between teaching and an alternative career, must have thrifty ancestors or a rich wife—

exactly so long will society continue to carry on the vital business of education with its left hand, and be lucky to come off as well as it does.

Pragmatism, a brave attempt to meet an overwhelming challenge, deserves not to be blamed for the excesses of those who have fallen in behind its banner. But one such excess, direct offspring of an evolutionary view of society, must go into the record. It is the idea that since social change is desirable the schools must be made the instrument of social change. If social change really *is* desirable, and there is agreement to that effect within the adult community, well and good. But it is adult society and not the school which is the legitimate and honorable battleground of social change. In terms of social evolution, as religion is the distilled essence of any culture, so education is the instrument of its continuity. Through education the young are fitted to participate in their culture and to preserve it. To make the schools, behind the backs of the adult community, so to speak, into instruments of operation against the culture, is not education, and certainly not sportsmanship.

Democracy has in its structure other and fairer means of change. Democracy will be preserved not by telling its young what to think, but how to think and giving them the means with which to think. The challenge of evolution to our own society is not to indoctrinate. It is a challenge to create.

THE GREAT REUNION

IT WAS Thomas Malthus, political economist, who furnished to Charles Darwin, naturalist, the vital clue. Since their day, political economy has been broken up into at least three separate disciplines—political science, economics and sociology. Likewise the naturalist has vanished and in his place we have an array of specialists. Yet more visibly than ever political life is enmeshed with economics and sociology, demanding a re-synthesis in theory and practice. Clearly, too, the problem of man's relation to nature calls for a new unity of viewpoint and understanding akin in spirit to that of the naturalist. Man is facing, in intensified form, two ancient problems—that of living with himself and that of making his peace with nature. We call them two problems. Actually we should see them as facets of the same greater problem, if we accept Darwin's view that man is a part of nature. The theologian, in his own language, puts it all very simply as man's relationship with God.

Back of mankind's ceaseless, thronging, troubled, glorious adventure there seems to be one compelling drive, over and above that of survival—the unending quest for order. It engages the energies and the thoughts of men everywhere. Yet how sadly men are divided by barriers of expression, of method, and of insight! And with what supreme tragedy the noble quest is perverted by the corrupting love of power! Distorted, too, by envy and resentment, dulled by apathy and selfish complacency, still the quest moves on as life moves on. Today the very facts of world politics express it far beyond any conscious intellectual or artistic synthesis. Government is everywhere entangled with economic and social issues, while political and religious doctrines have become almost inseparable. This is not to say that these aspects of experience have ever had separate existences. In simpler times they *seemed* more like separate entities.

In the field of social action (using that term in its widest sense) there is always a series of questions to be answered. What is true? What is possible? What is fair? What is expedient? What is advantageous, and to whom? The answers are seldom simple, often difficult, if not impossible. But there can be an order of priority and a quality of effort in seeking answers, and these measure the worthiness of motive, as results must prove the folly or wisdom of human choice.

There was from the beginning a curious duality in the reception of Darwinism by those content with the *status quo*. On the one hand, a competitive commercial and capitalist system was itself an expression of the struggle for existence and the survival of those best fitted for that struggle. On the other hand, the very social order itself rested upon a traditional acceptance of certain religious beliefs, whose disturbance in the growing atmosphere of social ferment was not comfortable to contemplate. A distinction should be made between this apprehensive view and the concern of those who, for no selfish reason, feared the purely spiritual effects of the new doctrine. It is probable that at least two political leaders, Gladstone, and much later, Bryan, belong with this latter group. For the defenders of privilege and their confused position there can be no such justification.

The term "social Darwinism" has been applied to a whole set of attitudes. These include, for example, race prejudice built on the assumption that some races (usually to be exploited) are lower in the evolutionary scale than others. From this view have arisen pious phrases such as "the white man's burden," and their self-justifying postulates. Belief in ruthless individualism and unrestricted competition, legitimizing the growth of great fortunes and corporate power, are other aspects of social Darwinism. Yet it is well to remember that exploitation and greed are far older than the idea of evolution, and that the greedy have had no more scruple in using half-truths or convenient doctrines than any other instrument which might serve their purposes at a particular time. Darwin is hardly to be blamed for man's inhumanity to man.

A more subtle and difficult aspect of social Darwinism is the eugenics movement, founded by Galton, Darwin's cousin, in 1883. A distinguished student of inheritance and of statistical methods, Galton interested himself in the possibility of improving mankind through heredity. No one with a working knowledge of biological principles, and certainly no one familiar with the practical business of breeding race-horses, dairy cattle, or hunting dogs, would question the importance of such a program. Moreover, there presently became available some detailed studies of the social cost of defective heredity, and, in the case of the Edwards family, the social benefits of exceptionally good breeding stock.

But objections to the eugenics movement were not slow in coming. Social scientists found reason to believe that bad environment, thwarting the promise of essentially sound heredity, was the most expedient point of attack. In this they were sustained by such an example as Lincoln, whose origin seemed to be from "poor white trash" (although the legend of a patrician ancestor in this instance will not down), and by the spectacular successes of immigrant stock of the humblest origin, given the advantages of a favorable environment in the New World.

In addition, a considerable number of psychologists were becoming aware of the power of skilled guidance in shaping personality, and of the difficulty of proving that the inherent capacities of any race, or social group within a society, were definitely superior or inferior. Such scientists joined hands with the sociologists in emphasizing the importance of nurture over nature. Euthenics thus arose, to supplement or oppose eugenics, according to the temper of its advocates.

Actually, in human breeding as in the art of teaching, there is such a vast accumulation of wisdom from trial and error that it is a bit foolish to write off the past for a completely fresh start. What countless times could we match these words from an old letter found in family files, and written by a father to his son:

"When you come to choose a wife, character is the first and indispensable quality. Then a good mind in a sound body, congenial tastes, education and social capacity. Wealth if possible, but at any rate an understanding of the importance of practical matters."

On the positive side, humanity has done and will continue to do some very tangible things to conserve good heredity, without benefit of studbooks. Meanwhile, the euthenists are justified in their insistence that a great deal more can and should be done to mitigate the evil and corroding effects of bad environment. This has become a live political issue throughout the world.

On the negative side, various political units have legalized voluntary sterilization of the unfit. Rational birth control, however, is less a negative than a positive measure, having as its objective a fairer chance for better nurture of those who are born. This is, in fact, a lesson from evolution itself, for both in plant and animal kingdoms as organisms advance from primitive to specialized, a greater proportion of parental energy and time is devoted to the individual offspring. Fish lay eggs by the thousands, give them little care and the young fry still less. The birds, higher on the scale, lay few eggs, incubate them and rear the young until they are ready to leave the nest. The human female produces usually a single egg for fertilization, and the human infancy is prolonged—ending legally at the age of twenty-one in our own country.

Moreover, in the modern world, regardless of creeds, it is generally true that a high standard of living results in a decreased rate both of deaths and births. Family size in the United States is inversely proportional to economic status, while Catholic Ireland with a now high level of subsistence, has overtaken Catholic France and Protestant Scandinavia in approaching a balance between birth and death.

Granting that a general improvement in education and living conditions—the aim of euthenics—will result in a decreased birth rate and ultimate adjustment of population to resources, there remain some pretty grim difficulties. Better environment will work—in fact, is working—in those countries which have some margin of safety between resources and population. But in the Orient, in parts of the near-East and Latin-America, the pressure upon resources is so terrific that any economic and sanitary improvement may be expected to increase population pressure for some time to come. Because of this fact the suggestion has been made that economic and educational assistance in all fields except public health be given to such areas, so as not to increase the rate of survival beyond a manageable degree. Only later, when the benefits of a better economy and higher literacy may have an effect in reducing the rate of birth, would full-scale modern preventive medicine be applied!

Back of all modern political systems lies one thought—that man is now charged with responsibility for his own further evolution. Such evolution has no concern with such matters as a more conveniently arranged and better built body. It has to do with the more immediate and everyday aspect of evolution, that is to say, the adjustment of behavior to fit environment. The notion of rigid, changeless political forms went overboard with the English Revolution which banished the Stuarts. Democracy anticipated Darwinism in providing the means of its own continuing adjustment and modification. It exemplifies a kind of Darwinism, without owing any of its basic concepts to Darwin. The same may be said of the free-enterprise system which has more or less accompanied it. The social Darwinists may have justified the growth of great corporate powers through ruthless competition, but the control of such expansion in the interests of freer competition among smaller units and individuals can be equally justified.

On the whole, democracies have been more inclined to make use of evolutionary principles in the practical arts of medicine and agriculture than to use them for purposes of doctrine. This cannot be said of the two great rival philosophies of the modern political world, fascism and communism.

Thus fascism has chosen to emphasize the evolutionary differences between human groups and between individuals. Much is made of the hereditary qualities of born leaders and master races. Power belongs, by this doctrine, to those who can grasp and hold it. Those who cannot are to be exploited or even eliminated by a process of utter ruthlessness, now known as genocide. Since the whole movement rests upon grounds which are not scientifically tenable, science itself must be brought into conformity. Scientists are compelled to give directed verdicts, and those not of the master race are thrown out. The interest of the Fascist state becomes the test of "scientific" truth.

Goebbels, who had gleefully propagated biological and social falsehoods under the guise of science, lived to see and record the disaster which came from interference with freedom of inquiry in the physical sciences. By 1943 the quality of German research in fundamental physics had so fallen off as to lead to serious if not decisive handicaps in the air and undersea. Freedom of inquiry has never been more dramatically justified than it was among the allied nations of the West who opposed Germany and outdistanced her in scientific and technological achievement.

It can, of course, be argued that one group of sciences might have been controlled and another left free. Goebbels evidently thought so. This argument does not impress one familiar with the intimate bonds which more and more tightly thread back and forth through all the sciences. And it is patent nonsense to anyone who understands the psychology of creative scientists in general. A modern political power which tampers with scientific truth in any field is writing its own death warrant, regardless of any temporary advantage that may seem to result. The human mind has often been restrained, but history is perfectly clear as to the inevitable consequences. Bar truth from the open market and it becomes a more powerful bootleg commodity than corn liquor, and more explosive.

The relations of the third great modern political doctrine—communism—to Darwin's doctrine are much more intricate than those of democracy or fascism. Marx had developed his ideas before he read Darwin. But he saw in the idea of natural selection a scientific basis for his system, and his followers still reflect this view.

While it is of the utmost importance that Marx be understood clearly and judged fairly, the task is extremely difficult. He was a student of human society who made valuable contributions to knowledge. But he was also an advocate of social revolution—an applied scientist whose wish, if not father to his thought, is certainly not easily to be separated from it.

In principle the objective of communism is the widest possible diffusion of social and economic opportunity. It has no monopoly on this idea, but its enemies deceive only themselves by closing their eyes to this, its most fundamental appeal. As a student of society, Marx had to have a working theory of social structure and process. As an advocate of change he required a theory of action. The two had to be consistent and, in his judgment, expedient.

The earmark of ordinary scientific inquiry, even in social problems, is its tentative character, its willingness to examine and sift new evidence and to revise all previous assumptions if that becomes necessary. But Marx took over a rigid philosophical device which Hegel had used to describe the development of ideas—the familiar dialectic of thesis, antithesis, and synthesis. For Marx this became the valid description of social process. Crudely stated, a situation sets up its opposing forces and tendencies, is destroyed by them, and a new order—the resolution or synthesis—is established. Marx was viewing a scene in which material situations were visibly affecting human welfare, while the realm of ideas was virtually a world apart from the injustices of the industrial revolution. He repudiated idealism and sought material explanations and instruments of action. Thesis, antithesis, and synthesis were transposed to the field of physical process as dialectic materialism.

The key to social process was found in the economic struggle, and economic classes were the visible expression of that struggle. Historically the domination of the aristocracy (thesis) had given rise to a struggle with the bourgeoisie (antithesis) and its resolution by the transfer of economic power to this latter, middle class (synthesis). But this new control (thesis) was based upon exploitation of the working proletariat whose coming revolt (antithesis) was destined to result in a new transfer of power (synthesis).

Such, in great simplification, is the theoretical skeleton of Marxism. It had the great merit of recognizing, at long last, the fact of social process. It had the additional merit of emphasizing the economic factor. And it had the advantage of being explicit and thus conveniently adopted to prophecy. Its application in social analysis, as in Trotsky's brilliant account of the Russian Revolution, can be hypnotically convincing.

Dialectic materialism, however, has none of the cautious, tentative character of Darwin's analysis of biological process. It is too rigid to fit either the mathematical or experimental analysis even of processes of a far simpler order than those of human society. The chemists, for example, have given considerable attention to the oxidation of sugar. Using only a few variables, in comparison with the many which enter into biological and social processes, they have discovered an amazing number of possible outcomes, to which no simple syllogism will apply. In addition the doctrine of dialectic materialism has, in application, a curious internal contradiction which its more astute critics have noted. If the revolution of the proletariat has the inevitability of natural law, why should anyone subject himself to iron discipline, risk freedom and life, and disrupt the lives of others to bring on what is inevitable? This criticism has had its answers in neo-Marxian literature, but the answer which drowns out all doctrinal statements is the cold fact that extreme Marxism has become politically effective through the seizure of absolute power by the few over the many.

Why then the repeated affirmations of modern Communist Marxism of loyalty to "Darwinism, as presented by Darwin"? Unquestionably, the theory of evolution seemed a valuable and opportune ally. Science, until the time of Darwin, was not a serious threat to the traditional assumptions of divinely appointed order which had, it must be confessed, too often condoned social injustice, yet which had a tremendous grasp on the imaginations of men, privileged and oppressed alike. Darwinism seemed to be a useful weapon, despite the fact that it could cut both ways. Darwinism was seized upon as a system of natural, hence physical and material causation. The idea of a ruthless struggle for existence was as ready made for the Marxians as for the advocates of unbridled individualism. And the former, by extending it to social groups, were the more intelligent, though they failed to reckon with the relative fluidity of the class system in Western Europe and the United States.

Fortunately, too, for Marxian purposes, Darwin himself was unclear as to the problem of individual differences, heritable and otherwise. In the then state of knowledge, he had no choice but to consider the possibility that environment might *produce* favorable variations as well as select them. For a philosophy of social action bent on taking over and controlling the environment, this was a most congenial notion. Nor could anything be less convenient than the idea that economic privilege was in part at least the result of innate differences in capacity among individuals and groups.

But by the time the Russian Revolution had become an accomplished fact the existence of definite heritable differences in capacity had been established. So had the general laws of their material basis. Nor, even to this date, has there been generally acceptable evidence that environment does induce favorable variations that can be transmitted. Here was materialism with a vengeance, and for a time the officially sponsored Soviet science made magnificent contributions to the new science of genetics, applying it successfully, too, in the breeding of animals and plants.

Western scientists who were personally sympathetic with the avowed Communist ideal of perfect economic justice, of free speech and inquiry, and the control of production for the common good, gladly collaborated in these inquiries for a time. Eventually some of them, at least, were alienated by the harsh measures used to sustain and spread communism. Nor did they like the growing tendency to dictate to scientists what they should do, and even what they should find out.

Today all of the famous Mendelian scientists in Russia have been silenced. The purely political aspects of this change do not concern us here, even if they could be unravelled. For our purpose it is enough to know that the official policy of this Marxist government is to disavow modern genetics and to subscribe to a form of Darwinism that includes belief in the inheritance of acquired characters—the old Lamarckian doctrine. The spokesmen of this belief assert that, by controlling environment, they can produce such variations in plants and animals as they desire. And the inference is clear that human beings, living in their favored social environment, can transcend inherited limitations.

For this viewpoint no evidence that will satisfy the canons of Western science is as yet forthcoming. True, Western scientists are not merely skeptical about the possibility that acquired characters may be inherited—they are often dogmatic. This is bad for them, bad for science, and bad for the world, even though they may be right, as they probably are. Once bitten, twice shy. At least three times in recent decades has evidence in support of the Lamarckian idea been brought forward. One report was shown to involve fraud, a second inexcusable carelessness, and the third a source of technical error which was later discovered.

The third instance reflects nothing but the highest credit on the scientist involved. It illustrates the kind of problem to which Darwin opened the door. And finally it involves a question of world-wide political interest. For these reasons it may be described—truly a story of mice and men.

This third instance had its beginnings in 1921, when two scientists at the University of Illinois were studying the sense of balance, because of its importance in aviation. They were observing the effects on white rats of long residence in horizontal whirling cages. After an experience of this kind the animals naturally showed some motor disturbance, but usually recovered.

Eventually, however, some offspring of the test animals were born with a penchant for travelling in circles. It looked very much as though the effects of parental experience had been inherited.

When motion pictures of the experiments were shown at Toronto, the conclave of scientists was greatly impressed, until some skeptic in the back of the room called out "Are you sure that those animals did not have a hidden strain of the 'waltzing' habit in their inheritance to start with?"

The investigator answered, not with recrimination, but with the honest admission that he did not know. The studies were continued and eventually it was shown that the phenomenon was due to a diseased condition of the inner ear and was in no way a matter of inheritance. Thus vanished another intriguing vision of the inheritance of acquired characters. And thus the whole issue, so far-reaching in its possible implications, was settled in an atmosphere of complete good faith, free inquiry and open criticism. The burden of proof, and it is a heavy one, still rests upon those who believe in the inheritance of acquired characters. The final answer will come only through pursuit of the truth in Darwin's own spirit of patient and candid inquiry.

Any political and social system which attempts to constrain that spirit is building upon sand. It is the great destiny of human science, not to ease man's labors or prolong his life, noble as those ends may be, nor to serve the ends of power, but to enable man to walk upright, without fear, in a world which he at length will understand and which is his home. Charles Darwin did not kill the faith of mankind. He wrought mightily, and others with him, for a newer and greater faith—faith in universal order, whose secrets open themselves to men truly free to question, to communicate and to arrive at agreement as to what they have seen.

LIFE AND WORKS

Charles Darwin, son of a physician, grandson of Erasmus Darwin, poet and physician, and of Josiah Wedgwood, potter, was born at Shrewsbury, England, Feb. 12, 1809. Studied medicine briefly at Edinburgh, graduated at Cambridge in 1831, intending to take Holy Orders. His real interest, however, was in natural history, and he became naturalist on H. M. S. *Beagle,* making extensive studies in the southern hemisphere, 1831–1836. Began study of origin of species in 1837, publishing his great work on that subject in 1859, following it with later work on evolution and plant behaviour. He married his cousin Emma Wedgwood in 1839, and lived in semi-retirement at Down in Kent from 1842 to his death on April 19, 1882. He did not originate the idea of organic evolution, but was the first to amass overwhelming evidence in support of it and, with Alfred Russell Wallace, to present convincing arguments for natural selection. His work on the geology of South America alone would have won him permanent distinction in science. His genius lay in his capacity for sustained effort—despite continuing ill-health—and in the open-minded, patient, tentative attitude with which he approached scientific problems. He is buried in Westminister Abbey. His influence in life and thought continues to grow with the years.

A BRIEF BIBLIOGRAPHY

American Association for the Advancement of Science, *Fifty Years of Darwinism*. N. Y.: H. Holt & Co. 1909.

Barlow, Lady Nora, *Charles Darwin and the Voyage of the Beagle*. N. Y.: Philosophical Library. 1946.

Barlow, Lady Nora, *Charles Darwin's Diary of the Voyage of H. M. S. "Beagle"*. Cambridge: The University Press. 1934.

Barzun, Jacques, *Darwin, Marx, Wagner*. Boston: Little, Brown & Co. 1941.

Conklin, Edward G., *The World's Debt to Darwin*. Proceedings of the American Philosophical Society 48. 1909.

Darwin, Charles R., *Journal of Researches into the Natural History and Geology of the Countries Visited During the Voyage of H. M. S. Beagle Round the World*. N. Y.: E. P. Dutton & Co. 1906 & 1912. (Everyman's library)

Darwin, Sir Francis, *The Life and Letters of Charles Darwin*. N. Y.: D. Appleton & Co. 1925.

Hingston, R. W. G., *Great Lives: Charles Darwin*. (One of a series) Duckworth. 1934.

Huxley, Thomas H., *Lay Sermons, Addresses and Reviews*. N. Y.: D. Appleton & Co. 1871.

Osborn, Henry F., *From the Greeks to Darwin*. N. Y.: C. Scribner's Sons. 1929.

Pearson, Karl, *Charles Darwin,* 1809–1882. London: Cambridge University Press. 1923.

Romanes, George John, *Darwin and After Darwin*. Chicago: Open Court Publishing Co. 1892.

Thomson, John Arthur, *Darwinism and Human Life*. N. Y.: H. Holt & Co. 1909.

Ward, Charles H., *Charles Darwin: The Man and His Warfare*. London: J. Murray. 1927.

Wells, Geoffrey H., *Charles Darwin: A Portrait*. New Haven: Yale University Press. 1938.

SELECTIVE INDEX

TWENTIETH CENTURY
LIBRARY